BEEKEEPING

Apiary Tools
Photograph by the Author

Preparation of Syrup—Sugar, hot water, measure and rapid feeder
Note : No Chemicals
Photograph by the Author

BEEKEEPING

A Guide to the Better Understanding of Bees Their Diseases and the Chemistry of Beekeeping

by

GEORGE A. CARTER, *B.SC., A.R.I.C.*

2013
BIOTECH BOOKS
Delhi - 110 035

ISBN 81-7622-111-2

Published by : **BIOTECH BOOKS**
1123/74, Tri Nagar,
DELHI – 110 035
Phone: 27382765
e-mail: biotechbooks@yahoo.co.in

Showroom : 4762-63/23, Ansari Road, Darya Ganj,
NEW DELHI - 110 002
Phone: 23245578, 23244987

Printed at : **Chawla Offset Printers**
New Delhi – 110 052

PRINTED IN INDIA

CONTENTS

FOREWORD

In recent decades there has been, with a few brilliant exceptions, a considerable sameness in the smaller "bee-books": *Bees and Honey* is an outstanding exception.

For much of the older teaching Mr. Carter has no use, but never does he fail to offer alternative guidance, or to give reasons for his beliefs: these alone would bid the book welcome.

In addition, however, we find discussed in this little book subjects cursorily dismissed even in the larger volumes, while other matters are expounded of which bee-keepers may justly plead ignorance, for never before have they been given the opportunity of seeing them mentioned in any text-book.

From this book, moreover, the reader will gain, not only new knowledge in matters pertaining to bee-keeping: not only enhanced pleasure in the diversities of the craft: but an altogether better understanding of the fundamentals underlying the proper handling of bees and honey.

That publication should take place now consorts well with the enthusiasm and enlightenment which have pervaded the fraternity, and will go far to show that the aims of farmers, fruit-growers, and bee-keepers are in accord, their needs interdependent, and their co-operation vital for the national good.

149, Harley Street,
London, W.1.

A. L. GREGG

ACKNOWLEDGMENTS

The author is greatly indebted to Mr. H. J. Wadey, Editor of *Bee Craft*, who has kindly read the MSS on the bee-keeping matter ; to Dr. C. G. Butler and Mr. P. S. Milne, of the Bee Research Laboratory, Rothamsted, for their help and advice on the chapters on the Diseases of Bees, and for photographs ; to Dr. H. G. H. Kearns, of Long Ashton Research Station, for his suggestions on the chapter on Fruit Sprays and Bees ; and to the " Shell " Film Unit for permission to use the photographs from their films, " Fruit Spraying " and " Protection of Fruit."

To Dr. A. L. Gregg thanks are expressed for his suggestions and constructive review of the complete work, and for his " Foreword."

A debt of gratitude is also due to Mr. P. C. Thornton for his advice and assistance in seeing this book through the press, and for help freely given in many ways.

Finally, the author wishes to thank his wife, whose help and patience throughout in shaping the book have been invaluable.

Ashtead, Surrey.

I—THE SIGNIFICANCE OF THE HONEY BEE

LET us be frank ! Most people keep bees to obtain honey, and value their bees on this basis. Nature, however, has other ideas ; and it is the intelligent bee-man's aim to wed the two successfully.

Primarily the part played by the honey bee (*Apis mellifica*) is that of pollinator. Without pollination fruit trees would either not yield, or else produce but little fruit ; and from clover would be harvested only a fraction of the seed which is obtained when insects have access to the flowering plant. Also, of course, without pollen, the bee would be unable to rear its brood, and the race would die out. Therefore, bees and flowers are complementary the one to the other.

Scientific tests carried out by agricultural research men, have shown that the yield of fruit is considerably increased when a powerful stock of bees is allowed access to the trees. Peaches grown under glass only set a very small quantity of fruit, unless the tedious and uncertain operation of hand-pollination is carried out. If a colony of bees is placed in the house, the increase in fruit is enormous.

When bees carry pollen from the male to the female flower in cucumbers, there is a notable increase in the numbers of fruit, which is also much larger and of fine shape.

Not all flowers depend on insect pollination. Some plants are self-fertile, that is, capable of carrying out pollination within their own blossoms without the help of outside agencies. Other plants produce pollen which is meant to be wind-borne ; some grains are fitted with wings, and in such cases the pollen is carried from one flower to another by the breeze.

Flowers which are to be pollinated by insects always

exhibit attractions to that end. There is a path of contrasted colour, called honey-guides, leading from the edge of the petal to the nectaries ; sometimes also a scent is given off by the flower. Pollen in such flowers is abundant. Some pollen-flowers, however, such as the rose and poppy, do not produce nectar.

Pollen grains are contained in the anthers of the flower, and when these are ruptured the pollen is freed. While seeking nectar, this pollen is deposited on the visiting insect, which when it visits the next flower of the same kind touches the female part (the pistil) and thus fertilisation takes place. When collecting pollen, the bee almost invariably visits the same kind of plants.

Pollen intended to be carried by insects is found to have grooves, or else projections, on its surface, to facilitate transport.

Dr. Butler, of Rothamsted, has stated (*Annals of Applied Biology*, August, 1943) that there are insufficient colonies of bees in large orchards ; and in general it is the hobbyist bee-keepers located throughout the country who provide the bees necessary for the pollination of crops. He also points out that the honey-bee is the one insect concerned in pollination whose scene of activities can be controlled to some great extent.

In other countries the value of the honey-bee is appreciated, and steps are taken to make use of it ; only slowly in Britain is the significance of the honey-bee coming to be recognised. It is of prime importance to the country as a whole, that in difficult years, especially such as war-time, the number of colonies be maintained in an efficient state to carry out the work for which Nature intended them.

II—THE MODERN HIVE AND APPLIANCES

THE first difficulty facing the beginner in bee-keeping is the choice of the hive. Usage and hoary tradition have led to the W.B.C. type of hive being adopted by the majority of the old-style bee-keepers. This hive is cumbersome and more expensive than the modern and much more workable American-type hive, and no further space will be devoted to its description.

This leaves the choice of three frame sizes, the Langstroth, the Modified Dadant, and the British standard. The Langstroth frame is standard in the Dominions and in most of the U.S.A., the dimensions being 17⅝ inches by 9⅛ inches. The Modified Dadant is a larger size, 17⅝ inches by 11¼ inches, and is used mostly in the U.S.A. and the U.S.S.R. One or other of these two types is used by the larger honey-producers in his country.

The third size is the smallest, being only 14 inches by 8½ inches. This is employed in the W.B.C. hive and in the modern British-American hive known as the "National." Owing to its small cell capacity, it is necessary to run a double brood-chamber. In fact, with the British standard frame, some advanced bee-men employ on occasion even three brood-chambers (and in the case of the National hive this means 33 frames, there being 11 frames to a box).

There has been, and still is, much unenlightened criticism of the American or single-walled hive, mainly from persons who have no experience of them.

It must be borne in mind that in the Dominions, America, and the U.S.S.R., honey-production is on a large scale, units of 5,000 hives being not at all uncommon. Producers, therefore, have to employ the hive with the least number of parts in order to reduce labour to a minimum. The objection that the National hive is cold and damp is not borne out by experience of the commercial producers in this country. One of the largest farms, that of Mr. Gale, on the exposed

Wiltshire Downs, has over 1,500 colonies, all in this type of hive. Mr. Manley, author of *Honey Production in the British Isles*, runs over 1,000 in Oxfordshire.

The flat, metal-topped roof, which permits tools to be rested on it, or for use as a stool when examining another hive, is absolutely water-tight. The square shape of the National hive permits the boxes to be placed either way (it is a fallacy to say that there is a " warm " and " cold " way of placing the frames ; there is no difference either way, as workers at Rothamsted have shown). There are no legs, the floor-board being kept off the ground by placing bricks under the four corners.

Do not acquire different types of hives and frames. Standardise on Langstroth, Modified Dadant, or British standard, and keep to the choice ; thus benefiting by their interchangeability.

The best subduing agent is smoke. Some bee-men use a carbolic cloth, but it has been observed that the queen is more difficult to find and that honey may become tainted when using cloths impregnated with carbolic. A good, well-built smoker, properly charged with corrugated paper, will keep alight for a long time. With normal stocks puff a little smoke into the entrance, wait about one minute, and then quietly open the hive. A few puffs of smoke over the tops of the frames should be all that is necessary to keep the bees from " boiling over " in panic or fury.

With a vicious stock, and one occasionally meets them, heavy smoking is necessary.

A mixture of chloroform, ether, and methylated spirits, in equal parts by volume, can satisfactorily be used on really vicious colonies by sprinkling a little (about an egg-cup full, no more) over a cloth placed over the frames. Another and thicker cloth, or wooden cover, should be placed over this to prevent loss of fumes by evaporation. The queen should be found in such circumstances, and destroyed. If the stock is re-queened, in due course the temper should improve as the new queen's progeny gain numerical ascendancy.

The use of such a means of subjugation, is, however, not

recommended as a normal procedure, but only for very vicious stocks.

Manipulation

Combs should only be removed from the hives on warm days. One is naturally anxious in spring to get working among the bees. Although there are usually many bright, sunny days at that period of the year, the wind, unfortunately, often has a keen edge, when, if combs are removed from the hives and exposed, much chilled brood may result. Normally, therefore, choose warm, sunny days, and if possible, about mid-day or early afternoon, when the hive is less crowded owing to the absence of many foraging bees.

Do not manipulate bees on wet, windy, and cold days, or late in the evening when the darkness of night is already gathering. One should allow plenty of time for carrying out the work until one has become thoroughly experienced and confident.

In the early days a beginner is, quite naturally, somewhat nervous and slow at the work. It is then that the benefit of warm and windless days will be realised and the prolonged exposure of the combs will not be such an upsetting matter, either to the bee-man or his bees.

Avoid jarring frames, and always handle them so that there is no danger of the combs falling out. It is best to remove the outside comb, quickly examine it for the presence of the queen (look along the bottom underneath of the comb first) and then place it in the shelter of an upturned hive roof or of an accommodating box. The space thus given by removal of one comb allows of easy removal and replacement one by one of the other combs if it is decided to examine all. Removal and replacement should be done steadily ; no bees will be crushed then.

Site and Situation

Although it is often stated that colonies of bees kept in large cities frequently yield considerable quantities of honey, this is the exception rather than the rule, and the statement should be regarded with reserve. Where the bees are within a few hundred yards of large areas of park-land, for instance, Hyde Park or Regents Park, it is possible to maintain a very few colonies and expect a yield of honey. But to obtain surplus honey the bees need sources of nectar in quantity.

The economic range of flight of the honey-bee is within a circle of one-mile radius. Stories of bees traversing many miles to and from the source of nectar and obtaining large harvests thereby are fantastic.

When about to set up colonies, study carefully the lie of the land. Avoid placing stands within a few hundred yards of the sea or an expansive lake ; obviously the waters will not furnish nectar.

III—THE NECTAR FLOW

Pollen and Nectar Plants

Correctly speaking, one should not refer to the honey-flow, but to the nectar-flow, since the plants yield nectar, not honey.

Honey is the product obtained after the bees have processed the nectar.

The first condition governing the nectar-flow is acres of the principal nectar plants—wild white clover, sainfoin, charlock, willow-herb, for instance—at their right flowering period for the bees.

The second requirement is favourable climatic conditions. A drying east wind is not conducive to a flow ; and both the soil and air temperatures must be sufficiently high to permit the nectaries of the flowers to give of their best. And, of course, sunny weather is desirable with some cloud. The conditions under which the nectar will, or will not, flow are not yet fully understood, but the humidity (that is, moisture content) of the air and also of the soil are other factors. Warm, moist days are good.

Having got the right flowers under the right climatic conditions, there still remain the questions of altitude and of composition of the soil and sub-soil. The heathers are an example of the effect of altitude ; heathers growing on low-lying land do not yield, whereas those flourishing over a certain height yield freely in due season. As for soil and sub-soil, most flowers of the *Leguminosae* family, such as clovers and sainfoin, yield at their best when growing in warm situations over chalk or limestone. Clovers on heavy, damp soils are not so good, except in very hot, dry seasons.

Not only does the nature of the soil and sub-soil govern the quantity of yield, but it is also probable that it has an influence on the aroma, flavour, and colour of the honey. This accounts for authorities in different localities giving wholly different descriptions of honey from one or two main sources.

A journey from east to west across England, from, say, Colchester through Bedfordshire and Oxfordshire to Herefordshire, will show the same wild flowers but growing on entirely different-coloured soils. Not only do soils vary from county to county, but in the county itself, and even in extreme cases, in the same field will be found different soils, due to differing mineral content. Such variations, coupled with the multitudinous varieties of flowers, result in English honey being a delightful blend and not a product of uniform taste.

Bee-men will now realise why, even in the same district, year after year, their bees do not always give them honey of exactly the same colour and flavour, and why also the amount varies so much.

Bee-Flowers of England

The honey-bee depends absolutely on an abundance of pollen and nectar. All plants produce pollen, but not all of them are available to the bee for this substance or for nectar.

Nectar-secreting plants for the bee will be enumerated later; here it is intended to deal with the plants which provide the pollen.

Pollen Flowers

About mid-January the workers begin to make inroads on their stores of pollen which were amassed the previous autumn. There are but few flowers available for two or three weeks yet, and it is late January or early February before a very slight supply can be obtained from winter aconites and from early catkins.

Early in March, crocus adds to the store, with dandelion supplying most of the needs. Early March also sees the hazel (lambs' tails) out, and where box is growing in abundance (as in parts of Surrey, Kent, Buckinghamshire, and Gloucestershire) a very good yield will be obtained.

April will see some garden plants visited by the bees. Fruit trees, such as cherry, apple, pear, plum, and gooseberry will now be in full blossom, and if the climatic conditions are good, thousands of bees will be observed among the trees.

May brings in many more bee-flowers, tulips, hawthorn, holly, etc., and in June, poppies will be sought out. At this time, too, the clover family, together with charlock and sainfoin, will supply pollen.

During early and mid-summer, scores of plants yield pollen, and it is during late summer and early autumn that the bees collect as much as possible, ending with the ivy in late autumn. This pollen is stored in the cells and covered over with a layer of honey and capped with wax until required in January at the commencement of brood rearing.

Bees fed on sugar syrup alone, and having no access to pollen, can and do produce brood, but for a limited period only; and as that brood never matures, the colony perishes. Therefore pollen is absolutely vital to the bees. There is no fully satisfactory substitute for pollen.

Pollen grains vary from about 1/100th of an inch to the

A Modern Hive (Langstroth)
Photograph by the Author

National Hives in Winter
Photograph by the Author

Hazel Catkins

Photograph by the Author

The British National Hive

From the Author's film "The Modern Hive"

extremely small grains of about 1/2000th of an inch in diameter. Analysis has shown that pollen consists of fats, proteins, carbohydrates (sugars), cellulose, and a small amount of mineral substances (phosphates, potassium and calcium salts, etc.). The quantities of these substances present in pollens from various sources are different.

Most pollens are yellowish in colour, but some are greenish, blue, brown, or red. The colours of certain pollens are difficult to determine with accuracy, the contents of the grain being a semi-liquid which is sometimes transparent.

A list of typical pollen colours is given below. The colours were determined not *in situ* on the plant, but on pollen transferred to a microscope slide and examined under a suitable magnification; in some cases a black background was used. Pollen packed in the baskets of the bees may appear to be darker than the colour quoted for that pollen, probably owing to the effects of diffusion and refraction of light.

FRUIT	POLLEN COLOUR
Apple	Transparent, greenish-yellow.
Blackberry	Transparent, whitish
Loganberry	Transparent, whitish
Pear	Transparent, yellowish-green
Raspberry	Transparent, greenish-white
FLOWERING SHRUBS	
Berberis stenophylla	Yellow
Broom	Yellow
Buddleia globosa	Transparent, whitish
Buddleia alternifolia	Transparent, whitish
Hawthorn	Yellow
Ivy	Transparent, pale yellowish-green
Wild Clematis (Travellers' Joy)	Pale yellowish-green
GARDEN FLOWERS	
Aster	Amber yellow

Forget-me-not	Transparent, light bluish-green
Golden Rod	Golden yellow
Helenium	Yellow
Lupin	Bright yellow
Mignonette	Transparent, yellow-fawn
Poppy, Iceland	Golden yellow
Poppy, Oriental	Bluish purple
Poppy, Shirley	Yellow
Rose	Golden
Salvia virgata	Transparent, very pale green

WILD FLOWERS

Blue-bell	Pale yellowish-green
Charlock (wild mustard)	Pale yellowish-green
Clover (red and white)	Transparent, greenish-yellow
Dandelion	Yellow amber
Heather	Whitish
Poppy (common red field poppy)	Bright yellowish-green
Ragwort	Golden yellow
Rose-bay willow-herb	Saxe-blue
Sainfoin	Bright yellow
Thistle	Transparent, white

VEGETABLES, ETC.

Leek	Transparent, very pale green
Mint	Transparent, very pale yellow
Kidney bean	Transparent, very pale yellow
Thyme	Very pale green

HOW BEES GATHER POLLEN

The honey-bee has specially-modified legs, which are its tools for gathering the pollen. It makes use of all six legs, in well-defined stages of operations.

With the front pair, the fore-legs, it cleans off pollen which has fallen upon its head from the anthers of the flowers, and also transfers pollen from the mouth, after it has been moistened with honey.

The mid-legs, furnished as all legs are with hairs to act as pollen brushes, take each fore-leg alternately in their grasp and brush off the pollen on to themselves.

Now the hind-legs come into play. By means of the specially-placed hairs called the pectens, each of these two legs sweeps off a little pollen at a time from the alternate mid-leg. This pollen falls into a cavity called the " auricle " which is on the hind-leg so placed that a projection on the joint preceding it, fits into it when the joints are pressed together.

When pressure is applied, a little pollen is squeezed out on to the outside of the hind-leg, and collects in the concave depression fitted with specially-shaped retaining hairs, and known as the *corbicula* or pollen-basket. Here the pollen gradually accumulates, each addition from the diagonally-opposite mid-leg pushing the previous load steadily forward as the auricle is squeezed.

When the baskets are sufficiently loaded, the bee returns to the hive and performs a typical pollen-dance, accompanied by a characteristic waggle of the abdomen. This dance, coupled with the odour of the pollen, informs on-looking bees of the origin of the load, and they are thus enabled to find similar supplies. The bee then deposits her pollen into a cell by clinging with her fore-legs to the top edge, arching her abdomen, and inserting her pollen-laden hind-legs. The loads are detached by the mid-legs scraping them off on to the floor of the cell. Other bees take part in packing the pollen into the cells and sealing it off with honey.

During storage, complete changes take place in the composition of the " bee-bread," due to inter-action between the pollen and the honey used to moisten it. Pollen which has been damaged by frost or rain, if consumed by the bees, may lead to " May Pest " (which see).

NECTAR-SECRETING PLANTS

As far as the bee-man is concerned, English nectar-secreting plants can be divided into two main groups, primary and secondary.

In the primary class will be found those plants which are the chief source of nectar, and without which, in general, worth-while yields of honey would not be obtained. It is possible that the colour, aroma, and quantity of honey are controlled by the nature of the soil and sub-soil, altitude, and climatic conditions.

The principal member of this class is wild white clover (*Trifolium repens*). It produces freely under well-defined conditions, and these include a high air and ground temperature, in situations other than low-lying valleys, and preferably on chalk or limestone. The period of flow is long under the right conditions, being from the end of May to nearly the end of July, the main flow occurring about the middle of June. White clover has the advantage that it mainly grows on pasture land, and is thus not likely to be cut for hay in such a situation.

Sainfoin (*Onobrychis viciifolia*) comes next on the list of nectar-secreting plants, the two varieties of it giving a flow between them which extends from early June to early August, unless the farmer cuts it early, as he should, for hay, when, of course, it is lost to the bee-man. Sainfoin has an advantage that it gives a flow at a lower temperature than does clover. Sainfoin and clover both belong to the family *Leguminosae*.

The next plant, charlock or wild mustard (*Sinapis arvensis*) belongs to the family *Cruciferae*. It is a familiar annual, the yellow flowers being in evidence from May to August, mainly in corn fields. Like sainfoin and clover, it thrives best on chalk and limestone. It yields copiously.

Rose-bay willow-herb or fireweed (*Epilobium angustifolium*) belonging to the family *Onagraceae*, is a common plant where woodlands have been cleared. It flowers from July to late August, and is included in the primary list.

Finally, there is heather, or ling, family *Ericaceae*. This family numbers many members, but it is the variety *Calluna vulgaris*, the ling, which provides the true heather honey.

It flowers from July to September. It is thought that heathers only produce a generous nectar-flow above certain altitudes, and on certain soils, Dartmoor being an example. Strictly speaking, ling is only of prime importance in certain localities ; in others it may only produce nectar in very small quantities.

The list of secondary plants which yield nectar for the honey-bee can itself be divided into two classes. The first class contains the fruit trees—plum, apple, pear, and cherry—where they are grown in great numbers, on fruit farms of 50 to 1,000 acres.

The modern commercial orchard contains about 150 trees per acre, when grown as bushes or half-standards, and where under-crops of gooseberries and raspberries, etc., are present, extra good yields of honey are obtained by strong stocks placed in these plantations. Dandelions (*Taraxacum officinale* of the family *Compositae*) when permitted to grow beneath the fruit trees give an early flow. Other flowering trees and shrubs, including sycamore and holly, hawthorns and chestnut, are also sources of nectar. The flow is usually over by the end of May, and, as always, the amount is largely governed by climatic conditions.

The second class contains the many plants which are in flower at the same time as the main sources, but are either by no means as numerous, or alternatively not such heavy bearers. Members of the family *Leguminosae*, the various clovers, provide the chief secondary sources, and include alsike (*Trifolium hybridum*), purple clover (*Trifolium pratense*), and others.

In favourable years the lime trees provide heavy yields of nectar. There are three varieties of lime in general cultivation in Britain in the family *Tiliaceae*, probably the variety *Tilia vulgaris*, common lime, being the one which is of chief interest. *Tilia platyphyllos* (the large-leaved lime) occurs mainly in Herefordshire and parts of Yorkshire. Unfortunately, under certain climatic conditions which are all too frequent, instead of gathering nectar from the lime flowers, the bees collect honeydew, a secretion on the leaves of the tree.

Sycamores and members of the firs (family *Pinaceae*) also yield the undesirable honeydew.

In some seasons, on favourable soils, the hawthorn, *Crataegus monogyna*, of the family *Rosaceae*, yields a fair flow of nectar. Field beans, where extensively grown, furnish a good supply in early summer.

Lucerne, *Medicago sativa*, of the *Leguminosae*, adds its quota. It flowers from May to July, and does best, in general with other members of this family, on chalk and limestone.

Ragwort (*Senecio Jacoboea* of family *Compositae*) flowering from June to October, and growing in open woodlands, usually in company with rose-bay willow-herb, furnishes a not inconsiderable yield.

Blossoming from late June to August, the common blackberry (*Rubus fruticosus* of the family *Rosaceae*) is an important secondary nectar plant.

Two varieties of heather (as distinct from ling), *Erica tetralix* and *Erica cinerea* (the bell heathers), flowering from July to September, yield some nectar when growing in certain districts.

Bee-men situated near the marshes and saltings of Essex, when the sea-lavender (*Limonium vulgare* of family *Plumbaginaceae*) is found, can depend on this plant for a quite considerable yield during late July and August. It flowers from July to November.

Also in flower from July to October, and worked by the bees during late July, is the spear plume thistle (*Cirsium lanceolatum* of the family *Compositae*). This plant is to be found almost everywhere.

Travellers' Joy (*Clematis Vitalba*), growing on chalky soils south of Stafford, is a fair nectar plant.

The garden provides a modicum of nectar from such plants as thyme (*Thymus*), golden rod (*Solidago*), globe thistle (*Echinops*), catmint (*Nepeta mussini*), michaelmas daisy (*Aster*), sneezewort (*Helenium*), lavender (*Lavendula*), sage

(*Salvia*) shrubs like buddleia and cotoneaster; and a host of others.

In Great Britain there are at least 1,200 varieties of wild flowers, not to mention flowering trees and shrubs, and the vast majority of them grow in England. Most of these must contribute something, if only an infinitesimal amount individually to the honey crop.

Enough has been written, however, to show that it is from plants in the primary class (wild white clover, charlock, fireweed, etc.) and certain of those in the secondary class (blackberry, lime, various clovers, etc.) that our English honey is produced. It would not be practicable, therefore, in England, for the ordinary bee-man to plant specially for honey production; he would need scores of acres of land at his disposal.

Heather Honey

If the bee-man is determined to obtain this variety of honey, which is of a peculiar taste and consistency (and not to everyone's liking), he can transport his stocks to the heather. This can be accomplished with the modern British-American type of hive (the National) but can be a tedious job and a nightmare with the old-fashioned, double-walled hives. The advantages of taking bees to the heather are two-fold. They arrive there after the normal nectar-flow from other flowers is over and, in a good season, the bees should gather a surplus and provide much, if not all, of their winter food.

But it must be remembered that the colonies which are to be so transported must be specially treated to be at the right strength exactly at the right time. To obtain this condition requires much skill on the part of the bee-man, and lack of it explains the many failures among tyros, who have taken their colonies to known heather honey-producing areas. It is essential to head the stock with a July-reared queen; but the experience and advice can be gained, and the latter is best obtained from a man who has many successful heather trips to his credit.

Fruit Honey

Bees are frequently placed in commercial fruit orchards. Here a warning is necessary.

Well-run, large-scale orchards (of areas from 100 acres to 1,000 acres) carry out extensive spraying programmes to combat insect pests and diseases, as indeed they must if they are to obtain any great yield of first-class fruit, (when there is a concentration of one type of tree, without the equivalent concentration of the enemies of the pests those trees are heir to, then Nature has a habit of upsetting the plans of man ; hence chemical control is necessary where biological control would have balanced matters). One wash used contains lead arsenate (sometimes an alternative, calcium arsenate, is used instead).

Arsenates are poisonous to bees (this matter is fully dealt with in the chapter on Fruit Sprays and Bees) so that either an insect repellant must be used with arsenate sprays, or the bees removed from the orchards. The latter is perhaps the better policy, as by the time it is necessary to use arsenate washes, the petals will have fallen and the bees would not be seeking nectar from fruit blossoms at that stage.

It is further to be remembered that in most modern commercial orchards the soil beneath the trees is kept "clean cultivated," that is, weeds are ploughed-in during early spring, and frequent harrowing, etc., carried out during subsequent months, to keep the ground clear of weeds. Hence in such orchards, the bees would find little sustenance after petal fall, and should be removed just at about 50% petal fall, and certainly before 80% petal fall, at which stage nicotine and arsenic sprays are applied. It is realised that plums, pears, and apples have a habit of being in blossom at different times, but unfortunately one cannot alter that fact, and the bee-man has to decide in the light of his own cbservations, when it is no longer economic to leave the colonies in the orchards.

In passing, it may be mentioned that in the case of plum orchards, if there are any dandelions in flower beneath the trees, then the bees seem to prefer to work them rather than the plum blossoms overhead. Possibly this is because the nectar in the dandelion is more abundant and accessible than in the plum blossom.

Of course, atmospheric and ground conditions must be right before a flow can be expected from either plums or weeds, or in fact, from any kind of blossom. A protracted winter and cold spring, followed by a cool, early summer, are conditions which lead to a low ground temperature, and hence lessen the nectar-flow, especially if sunshine has been below average.

IV—WINTERING

As with many other crops, the seed is sown the previous autumn. This means, in effect, that bees are prepared in late August or early September for the winter rest and early spring work.

The first condition of good wintering is a dry, water-tight hive. Damp is the greatest enemy of bees. Next see that there is a laying queen present, and at the same examination make sure that pollen-laden combs on either side of the brood nest are on the outside. Plenty of pollen is absolutely necessary, but if the pollen-laden combs are placed in the middle of the brood-box, it is likely that the queen may not lay beyond this "barrier." Re-shuffling of stored combs should not take place after July.

Estimate the weight of stores. A colony needs between 30 and 40 lbs. of sealed stores to carry it over to the safe period in spring. Then see that there are plenty of young bees present, on all 10 or 11 frames.

It does not matter which position the frames take in the hive ; either at right angles to, or parallel to, the entrance makes no difference to their wintering, or any other state.

The best packing for bees is—young bees, pollen, and sealed stores. Always leave a super of honey with the bees over winter, taking care to remove the queen-excluder. Many colonies have died-out because the excluder has been left between the queen in the brood-box and the super of stores.

If stores are not sufficient, then feeding must be resorted to. Use only large feeders, and feed rapidly. Measure into a large pan, pints of boiling water, and add to each pint 2 lbs. of sugar. Stir until dissolved, whilst keeping the mixture hot.

There is no need to boil the syrup, and no chemicals whatever should be added. Allow to cool off somewhat, then pour into the feeder. Avoid spilling the syrup which would induce robbing.

Never use honey from outside sources to feed bees ; it may contain the seeds of disease. (See under " Foul Brood " in the chapter on Diseases of Brood). Cover the feeder with small sacks to keep it at the hive temperature, and replenish as soon as necessary. When feeding has been completed, that is in early September, remove the feeder, wash it thoroughly, put it in the sunlight to dry for a few hours, then store away until next season.

As for the colony, see that a sound crown-board or glass quilt is in position. A small piece of calico over the feed hole will permit moisture to escape during the winter. One small sack placed on top of the crown-board, and the hive roof replaced is all that is necessary. Make certain with the older type of hive that there is no packing whatever between the winter chamber and the other cases. Air must be allowed free movement, else damp and mouldy combs will result.

The roofs of the older type of hives should be secured by tying a cord right round the hive, passing it underneath and up the sides. Do not tie bricks on a rope and sling them over the roof. Winds cause the weight to strike the side of the hive all winter, with consequent unrest to the bees, undue consumption of stores, and activity at the wrong time, all of which lead to weakness and dysentery in spring.

There is no need to contract entrances unduly during the winter months ; indeed, some successful bee men leave the door wide open during this period. Beyond occasional outside inspection there is no need to worry about the bees, if the foregoing instructions have been carried out.

The New Year

About mid-January one may judge the condition of the hive by gently removing the roof and feeling the temperature of the area just over the feed hole. All is well if there is a slight but noticeable warmth in the centre, as compared with the area over the outside combs.

During winter time the temperature of the cluster is probably about 57°F., but may fall lower than this during spells of very cold weather, should the outside air temperature fall to below freezing point, 32°F. When this occurs the bees generate heat by movement, to raise the temperature again in the centre of the cluster to about 57°F. Bees contract or expand the size of the winter cluster according to whether the temperature outside the hive is low or high.

The temperature on the outside of the cluster may fall as low as 45°F., and even lower for short periods during frosts. As the spring advances, the temperature in the centre of the cluster increases until it reaches the neighbourhood of 93°F., when egg-laying proceeds.

As the weeks pass, and the sun is with us longer, the area of this warmth should increase.

February usually borrows ten days from May, and during this period the bees will fly quite freely. Observe the entrance to see if pollen is being brought in. If so, that is a fair sign. If there are no flights, place the ear near the entrance and sharply tap the hive. If there is no sudden buzz, the note, after rising, falling to a lower pitch, then inspection should be made. Normally one does not open the hive until late April or early May, but in such a case as this, desperate measures are necessary. If the colony is dead, otherwise than by starvation, a sample of the dead bees, and a centre frame (or others if suspicion is aroused) should be sent to the Bee Research Laboratories at Rothamsted, and full details given (age of queen, condition of colony in autumn, state of hive, etc.) for diagnosis.

If the examination shows that the bees are alive but foodless, then they must be fed syrup at once, whatever the weather conditions. Should there be only a handful of bees, it would be useless to try to save them.

Bee-men who employ modern methods do not need to resort to candy feeding, as with ample stores of pollen and food the bees are quite safe. A check-up of the food position should be made at the end of February or early March.

Spring

With the arrival of fairer weather in spring comes the urge to handle the bees. Beyond substituting a clean floor-board for the over-wintered one, an easy operation with the modern hive, but complicated and risky with the old-fashioned W.B.C., nothing should be done.

In late April, on a fine, sunny day, when cold winds are absent, the brood nest may be examined. Make sure there is a queen laying; the presence of eggs will advertise this without prolonged search for the queen herself. Ascertain that there is a supply of food in the combs; if not, feed at once.

At this point, if the bees are adequately covering the majority of frames, add a super of drawn-out combs if the bees have not been wintered with a super of honey over the brood-nest. This will ensure plenty of room for the queen's output of eggs.

Summer Management

It may be found during May and very early June that one colony is crowded with bees and brood, and well ahead of another. The latter may be assisted by transferring a comb of brood and eggs (without the queen, of course) to the less strong stock. An empty drawn-out comb should be put in the place of that which has been removed.

About this period the bee-man will be troubled over the question of swarm prevention. Involved and cumbersome methods of preventing swarms are of little value. The bee-man should study that condition of the colony, so aptly described by Mr. H. J. Wadey in his book *The Bee Craftsman* as the "Hive Mind."

An early swarm (up to June 6, in average years in average localities) is no catastrophe unless it is lost, but later swarms are of less value, unless the bee-man is looking for increase of colonies rather than honey crop. In any case, controlled increase, and not haphazard swarms, should be the rule.

A simple and effective method of management is to examine the colony every 8 to 10 days from mid-May to mid-July. If queen-cells are found, it can be said at once that their mere destruction will not stop the swarming impulse; it will only delay it, and thus time, the most valuable asset, is lost.

Should examination reveal cells, take a comb of brood and eggs, upon which the queen is present, and place it in an empty hive. Fill up with drawn-out combs. Remove the original colony (the parent hive) and put that containing the queen and frames in its place. The bees flying from the parent hive, and those already out in the field foraging, will join this colony and thus an artificial swarm is formed.

If the original (parent) hive had one or two supers with it, take the heavier one and give it to the artificial swarm.

The parent hive should be examined again in 3 days, and all queen cells except one destroyed. Better still, a young queen, if available, should be introduced. But be absolutely sure that a queen-cell has not already hatched and thus a virgin is loose in the hive.

If it is preferred to leave the stock to raise a queen of its own accord, make certain that she has mated and is laying within a week or so. Virgin queens are very difficult to find, and quite a fair percentage of stocks lose their queens on a mating flight.

One may be assured that all is well by inserting a comb of eggs (from which all bees have been removed). If a healthy virgin or young laying queen is present, the eggs will become worker or drone brood in due course, whereas if queen cells are promptly raised upon it, then disaster has befallen the virgin. By this addition of a comb of eggs, the bee-man is insured against loss by giving the colony a second chance to raise its own queen. Time is saved, and a possible crop obtained, by re-queening in the first place.

Of course, if a swarm should emerge before the periodic examination, it should be hived, preferably on frames of drawn comb. The hived swarm should be placed on the site of the parent colony after removing the latter and treating it as outlined before. If no drawn-out combs are available, then foundation must be supplied, and food given for a few days to enable the bees to build comb rapidly. If syrup is given, remove the feeder as soon as it is seen that 5 or 6 combs have been drawn out.

This method of dealing with pre-swarm and swarmed stocks is known as the Pagden system, and is the simplest. For other methods the reader is referred to Manley's *Honey Production in the British Isles*, an up-to-date and exhaustive treatment of bee-keeping.

Brood-rearing makes great demands on the stores and on water. As regards the former, few realise that probably the surplus honey (that is, the crop removed by the bee-man in August) represents only a fraction of the total gathered during the season, it having been estimated that a colony consumes about 400 lbs. of stores in the course of a year. As for water, quite considerable volumes are taken by the bees.

Except in the use of a frame feeder for water supplies for colonies in orchards, during spring spraying of the fruit trees (see under Fruit Sprays and Bees) bees can be allowed to fend for themselves in this matter, but the provision of a drinking place affords a convenient index of the nectar flow—good flow, few water-gatherers, and vice versa.

They are apt to be a nuisance in suburban areas, where they gather around kitchen drain-pipes, and needlessly alarm the house-wife. They seem to prefer this liquid and rain-water to pure distilled water due no doubt to the salts (not necessarily common salt—sodium chloride) dissolved therein. They can be weaned from this, by providing a drinking trough supplied with water to which a very little sugar has been added at first, to attract them. Then, when they have got the habit of visiting this place, it should be replenished with water to which common salt has been added at the rate of 1 ounce of the latter to 10 gallons of water. Rothamsted have shown that this quantity is the optimum amount; any increase of salt is unnecessary and may be repellent.

After about July 15, there is usually no need for further examination of stocks which have progressed normally. The main nectar-flow is from clover and willow-herb at this period, and usually ends in the last days of this month. The bees at this time become somewhat hot-tempered, and the honey crop is all the better for being left on the hive during the first few days of August, at the end of which it will be found that the bees have improved in their behaviour towards man.

Throughout all phases of bee-keeping, it is obvious that complete interchangeability of the hives and their equipment is necessary. Never, never, of course, interchange equipment from diseased stocks. Employ the same type of hive, same size of frames, and above all, use only worker foundation. The use of drone comb advocated some years ago, and now dying out in the face of more intelligent teaching, to say the least, limits the facile interchange of supers and brood-boxes. For instance, an unexpected swarm can be temporarily hived on a super of shallow worker comb or foundation, but to do so with a box of drone comb would lead to the production of thousands of unwanted and useless drones.

Also, the bee-man is strongly advised to keep a log of each colony, and of every significant operation upon it. A handy method is to write the record on a post-card kept in the hive. If it ever becomes necessary to call in outside help, then at least the visitor has some concrete evidence to guide him. Too often has the author been asked to deal with colonies, of the past history of which the owner had only a hazy, and often quite incorrect, idea.

V—HARVESTING

Removing Supers

One of the benefits of honey production is that the harvest of bumper seasons can be held over for use during lean years. But this is so, provided that sealed honey only has been extracted and stored under correct conditions.

In the first place, honey should be left in the hive for a few days, even for three or four weeks after the honey-flow has ceased, if only to give the bees time to seal most of it. They always leave a little uncapped for their own immediate use. About August 20 is a suitable time to remove supers. The combs should then be removed, after the supers have been cleared by means of a Porter bee-escape.

If the nights are very warm, the bees may not leave the supers under 24 hours, but eventually all or most will. Any stragglers may be brushed off with a wisp of grass. Make sure of course, before putting on the clearer board, that the escapes are working freely. A board fitted with two " double " escapes is most advantageous.

Select first the combs which are fully sealed. These should

Yellow Crocus
An early source of pollen

Photograph by the Author

Aconites
Photograph by the Author

Older larvæ assume a grey colour and may later dry up to form a kind of brownish scale. Cappings may appear as in American foul brood, but the "match-stick test" fails to show "ropiness" and of course *Bacilli larvæ* are absent. Further, all the brood in the affected areas will have died, not here and there as in American foul brood.

The remedy is to manipulate hives at only seasonable times, and to house colonies in sound, damp-proof hives.

Feeding—Use rapid feeders

Photograph by the Author

be extracted first. Extraction should be carried out in a warm, bee-proof room, as soon as possible after the combs have been removed from the hive, as when the honey cools, it becomes viscous, and more energy and time are required to extract it.

Combs which are partially sealed should be tested by holding the frame horizontally in the hands, and jerking violently downwards. If no drops of honey are forthcoming, then it is permissible to extract. Do not make this test in the vicinity of the hives, for if there is an accident, and the comb falls out of the frame, or much honey is ejected, then robbing might be set up.

It is very advisable to extract the fully-sealed combs first, bottling this honey separately. The partially-sealed honey should be extracted last, and the extract bottled for immediate consumption, as it is quite likely that this honey will ferment some time later. Do not, on this account, mix honey from sealed and partially-sealed combs.

Uncapping

There is no need to use steam-heated uncapping knives. Heating of water or of knives for uncapping unnecessarily complicates the work, and further, if the knives are not quite dry, the water thus added (though very small in quantity) will almost certainly cause fermentation to take place in the honey from partially-sealed combs.

Those bread or cake knives with square teeth, the cutting edge of which is about ⅛ inch long, are admirably suited to the work, especially when used cold. Experience has shown that the bread knife which is least successful in the purpose for which it was designed, is of great value for the cold uncapping of combs.

Only practice will ensure clean and neat uncapping, and each bee-man must evolve his own method and stance. Where there is a large number of frames to be dealt with, the drainings of honey will be quite considerable. In this case the apiarist had best invest in an efficient drainings appliance, of substantial material.

Extractors and Extracting

There are two types of extractors in use, the radial (suitable for large apiaries of 20 or more hives) and the tangential, for small outfits. An extractor which will accommodate standard brood frames is desirable.

With the radial type, the frames do not have to be reversed in order to empty the cells, whereas this operation is necessary with the tangential machine. The radial type suffers from the disadvantage that the speed must be graduated from slow at first, else comb break-downs will be frequent. It can be power-operated. The tangential extractor permits of quite rapid extraction and is very suitable for small apiaries. Both types should be firmly anchored whilst in use.

Honey should be run off from the extractor from time to time else the revolving parts will be immersed in the contents, making the machine difficult to operate. Honey should be strained before bottling, and a cone-shaped metal sieve is best used for this purpose. Never leave the tap open unattended for a moment ; one may forget and return to find a pool of honey on the floor.

There is no need whatever to run the honey into tanks (the so-called ripeners) unless it is desired to use wide, shallow tanks for bottling by some other person, whilst one carries on with the extraction. It is a fallacy to assume that honey when stored for any period in such containers will ripen. In fact, being hygroscopic, it will absorb water, and one of the conditions conducive for fermentation to set in later, will have been met.

Metal containers for honey should be lacquered inside, and both they and bottles must be spotlessly clean and absolutely dry. Lids should be put on as soon as the containers are filled.

If the honey can be stored in a cold *dry* place, so much the better. Stored honey should be examined occasionally for signs of fermentation. Should frothing occur, that container must be removed and dealt with at once. If the froth is only slight and the honey smells good, skim it off and use the honey beneath at once. If the froth is extensive, and the characteristic beery odour is very evident, the contents should be gently warmed to about 160°F., the scum removed until no more forms, and the residue used for cooking. But if only sealed honey is extracted, and stored in dry containers at low temperatures, fermentation will rarely be met.

Avoiding Trouble

Many bee-men seem to meet trouble with both bees and neighbours at extracting time. Both these issues could be avoided by the application of a programme based on a knowledge of the habits of the bee.

It is the scent of the honey which causes the robbing among bees in the apiary, and the congregations of hundreds of bees round the house during and after extraction.

The usual plan for small apiaries is to put the super-clearer boards on in the evening, and on the third evening remove the supers. It may be found that some supers still have some bees among them. They can be dislodged by being brushed off with wisps of grass, in the apiary, and the super should then be carried into the house. It is best to deal with one super at a time in this manner, leaving the others covered on the hive. Then return for the others singly. If all are taken off at once, and the bees brushed off at the hive-side, it is likely that more bees will settle on the super already dealt with.

This removal of honey should be left until as near dark as possible. Do not remove supers of honey in the middle of a warm day, or trouble will certainly arise with neighbours! Be sure to have more than enough bottles clean and dry, ready at hand, complete with lids. When dealing with only a few supers, it is best to bottle at once through a strainer, sealing every bottle as soon as filled.

Collect the extracted combs, replace the metal ends if used, and return them in their supers to the hives the same night, for cleaning up. (Combs stored wet are liable to ferment, and the larger wax moth does not appear to be repelled by wet combs). If the internal arrangements of the hives are thoroughly known, the replacement can be done without any disturbance. The job is extremely simple with the modern single-walled hive, such as the National.

The extractor should now be thoroughly cleaned. With a short length of hose-pipe swill down the internals with lots of cold water, allowing the drainings to run through a strainer to retain the wax. If the palm of the hand is used to rub down the sides whilst the water is freely flowing, a considerable amount of cleaning is done. All the water should be run down the drain, allowing plenty of cold water to flow after it. Then the contents of a large kettle full of hot water should be swished around inside the extractor *after* removing the trapped wax in the tap strainer. All this should be done the same night. Next day the extractor can be taken to pieces and left in the sun. If more than a few bees collect round it, then cleaning has not been properly completed.

The wax cappings should be left draining all night, and either *very early* next morning, or after sunset, placed in a suitable tray in one of the hives for the bees to clean up. These precautions, somewhat tiresome, will ensure that the bees do not create a nuisance. Large-scale apiaries, will of course, have efficient extracting equipment in suitable surroundings. Honey exposed anywhere will lead to trouble.

VI—VARIETY OF TOPICS

QUEEN INTRODUCTION

IT is a fact that very many queens are lost annually by amateur bee-keepers through lack of attention to detail in the matter of queen introduction. It is little use purchasing or rearing a queen only to lose her on introduction. The first step *before* introduction is to make absolutely certain that the stock is really queenless. If the bee-keeper has actually removed the queen before attempting introduction, all should be well on that point.

Should sufficient time elapse between removal of the old queen and introduction of the new, it is possible that queen-cells may have been raised ; a state of affairs which will lead to destruction of the new queen. Make sure that there are no queen cells present. If there is still any uncertainty regarding the whereabouts of the old queen and there are no eggs present, insert a comb of eggs less than 3 days old. If the stock is really queenless, the bees will raise queen cells on this comb. These cells can be cleared, and the new queen introduced.

Do not attempt to introduce a queen during a dearth of nectar, if the stock is being robbed, or if preparations have been made for swarming.

Another cause of loss of queens is too hasty examination after introduction. Wait at least one week after inserting the queen-cage before making an examination ; and then make it as brief as possible. There is no need actually to find the queen, the presence of normal eggs is sufficient warranty.

Sometimes after a queen has been introduced in the autumn, no eggs are found. This is not abnormal, and the queen may be induced to lay a few eggs if the stock is fed. If this fails, search for the queen, and if she is seen, it can safely be assumed that all is well.

The introduction of a queen to a stock long queenless, or to one with laying workers, is a matter of difficulty ; and the best plan is not to attempt it, but to split up the stock among other colonies.

There are various methods of queen introduction. The "direct" method is favoured by some of those who rear their own queens and are thus able without delay to transfer a comb containing the laying queen from the nucleus to the stock to be requeened. Leave at least seven days before looking to see if she was safely introduced.

Another direct method is one whereby the queen is run in at the hive entrance. The queen is placed in a wire cage at the entrance to the hive and released after the bees have been examining the cage for about 5 minutes. In most cases the queen will walk fearlessly into the hive. Re-cage her if she is attacked and try again in about thirty minutes time.

A third direct method is one in which the queen is introduced at nightfall through the inner cover of the brood-nest. This is known as the Simmins method.

The most popular and generally safest method in the hands of an amateur is by means of the mailing cage. Full directions are usually sent with the cages, which are of varying types, and these directions should be implicitly followed. The method depends on the generally-accepted fact that when a new queen has acquired the hive odour she will be accepted. The method ensures this by the design of the cage which is so constructed that the queen cannot be released until the workers of the hive have eaten their way into the cage through a tunnel plugged with candy. Failures with this method do sometimes occur, but if the conditions mentioned previously are observed, they are likely to be rare. Do not be in a hurry, especially in the final examination after introduction.

Renewal of Combs

It is good policy to inspect carefully the brood-combs each year, preferably at the spring examination. Those combs which are mis-shapen, not built down to the bottom bar, and contain an unduly large proportion of drone comb should be rigorously culled. Fresh frames of foundation should be put in their place, and thus a first-class condition of brood cells maintained.

With irregularly-built combs there are usually a number of under-sized cells scattered about. Also, with very old combs which have been constantly bred in, the cell size is slightly reduced, and thus a number of small bees will be produced. The culling of combs will avoid this chance of small bees being bred, and also eradicate the irregularities of comb surface, caused by production of queen-cells.

As workers do not reproduce themselves, the production of small bees is an acquired characteristic, and cannot have a permanent effect on the race ; since the queens which produce the eggs are themselves produced in cells whose size cannot be affected by the age or general shape of the comb.

Top Entrances

The top entrance, or top ventilation, is no new idea ; indeed Langstroth advised it many years ago. Recently the use of top entrances, especially as a means of top ventilation during winter-time, is increasing, especially in North America, on both Atlantic and Pacific sides of the continent, and as far north as Canada. Thus a very wide variation in climatic conditions is experienced, and in general, those who have given the method a fair trial, have continued its use, being convinced that it is for the betterment of the health of the colony.

It cannot be too often stated that the bee colony is resistant to extreme cold, but that it will succumb to damp. Opponents of the top-ventilation system state that the bees will be colder during the winter. Even if this is so, it does not matter ; what does matter is that the bees are in a drier condition.

Another objection which is raised to this method of ventilation is to the closing of the bottom entrance. It is said that the bottom of the hive would become clogged with debris and dead bees. Normally, only few dead bees are found on the floor in the spring. Moist air is lighter than dry air, and hence rises to the top of the hive. The few dead bees which are on the floor of the hive will lose their body moisture to the dry air, and thus dry dead bees are found there at the spring examination.

It would appear, in any case, that bees die *outside* the hive, even in winter ; and that the incidence of a very large number of dead bees on the floor, under any system of ventilation, is indicative of something seriously wrong.

Already, then, there are two schools of thought among the users of top entrances. Some advocate complete sealing of the bottom entrance, others advise both top and bottom ventilation. It is quite likely that the advocates of the sealed bottom entrance method are overlooking the fact that there are cracks where the air can enter, and thus provide for the ingress of fresh air. Further, the hive itself will " breathe," that is, draw in air during the cold of the night, and expel air during the very slightly higher temperature of the day. In other cases the air is drawn in by a system of fanning, at the top entrance, by the bees themselves.

Here is another case in point for the National type hive ; experiments with top entrances are easily carried out with it.

The Emergency Feeding of Bees

Occasion may arise when it becomes necessary to feed a colony of bees during winter. This occasion should never arise in the normal way of bee-keeping ; but should, for instance, the bee-keeper discover a colony in mid-winter, which is obviously in a state of starvation, then of course, something drastic has to be done.

If the stock is not fed somehow, then it will surely perish. If it is fed, then either it perishes in spite of, or because of, the feeding, or it survives and prospers ; and if the feeding is done in time, the latter eventuality is more likely to occur.

Feed then, not candy, but sugar syrup, thick and very

Wintering (1)—Glass quilts are quite satisfactory

Photograph by the Author

Wintering (2)—Plenty of bees, pollen, stores, but very little top packing

Photograph by the Author

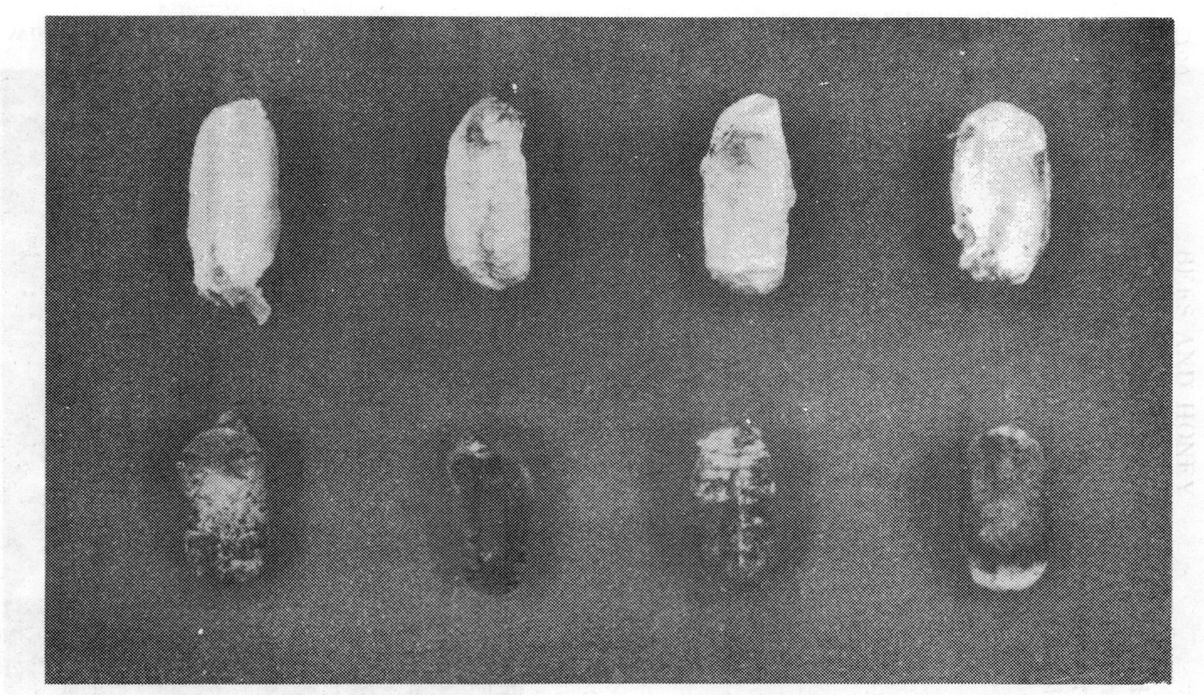

Chalk Brood—Mummies removed from cells. Top row : chalky-white mummies. Bottom row ; mummies with cysts,

Photograph reproduced by courtesy of the Bee Research Laboratory, Rothamsted

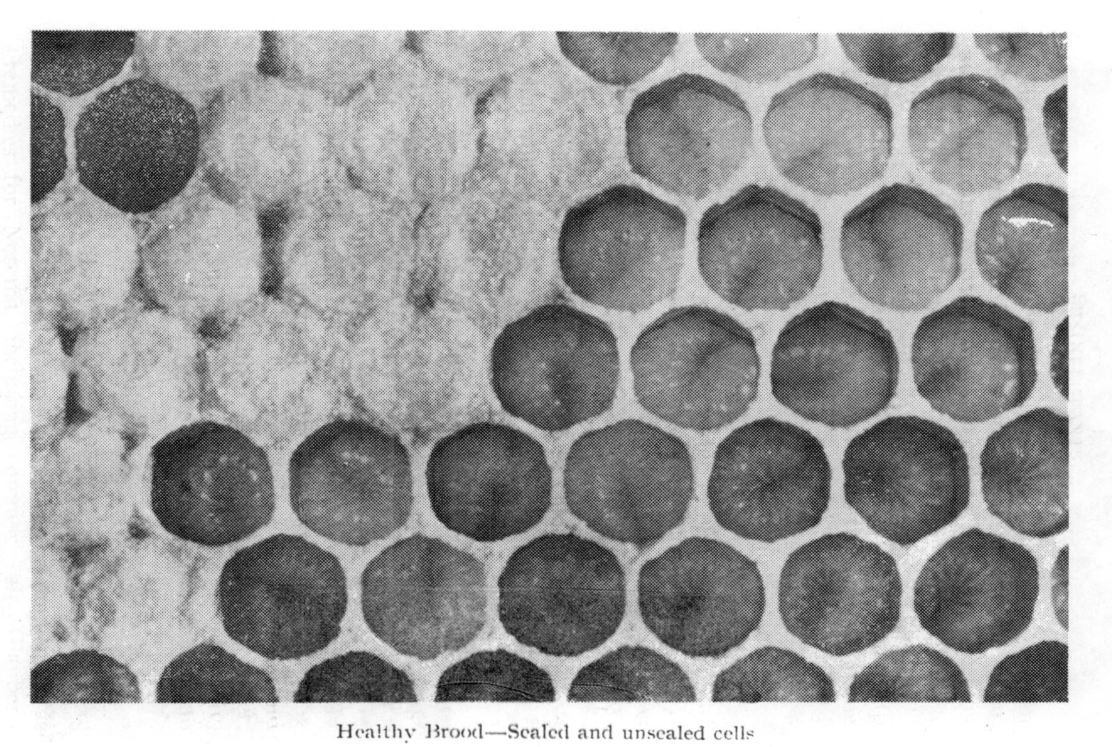

Healthy Brood—Sealed and unsealed cells

Photograph reproduced by courtesy of the Bee Research Laboratory, Rothamsted

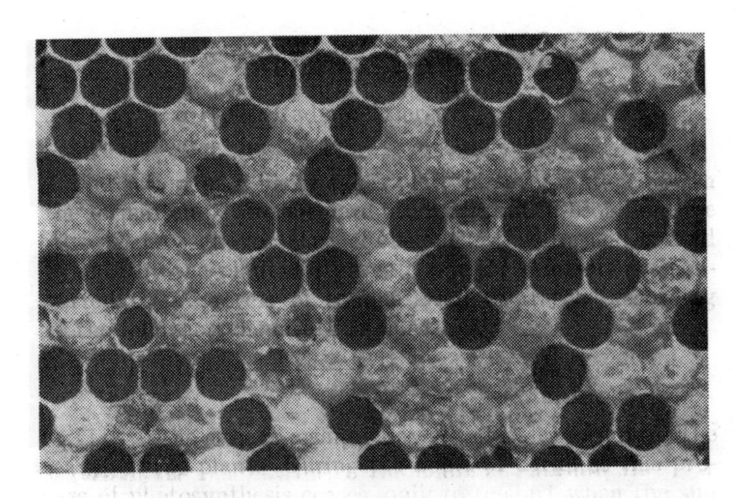

American Foul Brood

Comb with a few cells showing sunken cappings, some perforated

Photograph reproduced by courtesy of the Bee Research Laboratory, Rothamsted

American Foul Brood—Late stage of infection

Photograph reproduced by courtesy of the Bee Research Laboratory, Rothamsted

rapidly. Pure white sugar, cane or beet, and hot water are all that is required. Do not add any chemicals, a practice resorted to by many bee-keepers under the impression that this emergency feeding demands such addition. The reverse is very much the case. Watch the progress of feeding carefully. Supply in the first instance a small quantity, say a pint ; then next day increase to a quart, and carry on, with daily inspections until the bees have about 20 lbs. or so of stores. The colony will then have a reasonable chance of survival.

Moving Hives With Open Entrances

Recent American journals have given accounts of moving bees in hives with open entrances. The method appears novel, and it is claimed to be very simple. For the bee-keeper who wishes to remove one or two hives only, the method appears to be very suitable.

A motor transport is required, and this should have the engine running whilst the bees are being loaded. The hives are approached, presumably in the early morning or late evening, when there is little or no flying, and smoked. The hive is then lifted up, with the aid of an assistant, and placed on the transport. The vibration of the engine will keep the bees engaged inside the hive, whilst the next hive is being brought. The journey is then proceeded with, and one can imagine that no stops are allowed ! Arrived at the new site, the hives are smoked, and then carried to their prepared positions.

The method certainly seems all right on paper, for a very few colonies ; although the Americans move lorry-loads at a time. It is stated that, if the transport does stop, the bees certainly fly out, and cause alarm, if not trouble. The advantages include ease of removal and lack of suffocation troubles.

Plastic Hives

It is obvious that great strides forward have been made in

the use of plastic materials. Plastics are made from a phenol-formaldehyde process, which yields a product which can be moulded into almost any desired shape and possesses great strength. The materials can also be supplied in various colours, and can be made transparent, opaque, or translucent.

Plastic materials weigh much less than pine of the same volume. They are also non-inflammable, tasteless, odourless, and retain their shape indefinitely.

One property, however, possibly precludes their use for the manufacture of hives. Plastic materials are water-resistant, and do not allow the passage of moisture through them. If, as some bee-keepers maintain, moisture in the hive during wintering, passes out through the walls, it is possible that damp conditions might prevail. No doubt top ventilation would overcome this.

Hive inner covers and frames might well be made of this new material. The future will no doubt settle this matter ; meantime plastic feeders have already appeared on the show bench.

VII—THE DISEASES OF BEES

BEES, no less than other living creatures, are subject to diseases and pests. The diseases have existed in the past, and continue in the present. Foul brood, for instance was recognised, at least as early as 1832.

It is not necessarily true to say that, since the more intense bee-keeping has developed, there has been greater incidence of disease. The movable-frame hive has certainly enabled certain diseases to be transmitted more readily from colony to colony, but the knowledge of diseases has increased at a great rate so that the possibility of control is maintained. It was only in the case of the disastrous Isle of Wight disease (now described as acarine) that the disease and its results overwhelmed and almost obliterated bee-keeping in this country. But since then the life history of the mite causing the trouble has been worked out, and methods of control have been devised.

The importance of research work carried out by various persons, and by research stations such as Rothamsted, cannot be over-stressed.

The diseases and pests of bees can be divided into two classes: those affecting the perfect insect, and those the larva (brood). Fortunately the two classes do not intermix. Acarine does not affect brood, for instance; nor foul brood, a disease of the larva, affect the adult bees, though they can be infected and act as carriers. This chapter describes the diseases of the perfect insect. Diseases of the brood, and other troubles, not diseases or pests, are described in Chapter VIII.

Diseases and Pests of the Perfect Insect. (The Adult Bee)

Acarine	May Sickness or May Pest
Nosema	The Bee Louse
Amoeba	Wax Moths
	Paralysis

Acarine

The most common and widely-distributed affliction of the perfect insect is known as acarine disease. It is the result of the attack of a microscopic mite . . . *Acarapis Woodi*. The pest is less than 1/100 inch in length, and enters the thoracic tracheae) through the spiracles. Eggs are laid which produce male and female mites. The females produced leave the host bee and enter the spiracles of young bees, which happen to be in contact with the originally infected bees, lay eggs, and thus rear more mites.

This breeding in the breathing-tubes of the honey-bee weakens the host-insect, possibly by sucking the blood of the bee and by obstruction of the air-passage. Lack of oxygen and damage to the wing muscles result in the bee being unable to fly. Numbers of bees are seen crawling away from the hive, some apparently with dislocated wings.

A further sign is the content of the intestine, which is quite full with pollen residues, owing to the inability of the bees to take cleansing flights. The symptoms are usually only noticed in spring or autumn, although the pest may be present at any season.

The mite only attacks young bees, and the newly-emerged insect is the most susceptible ; after five days she is usually immune, but in some cases infection may take place up to a few days later. The mites can, however, increase in the bee attacked, but if there are no young bees in the colony, they cannot spread within the colony. Queens, drones, and workers can be attacked.

Fortunately, however, the pest is of such a nature that combs, hive parts, and tools of an infested stock are safe to use with a disease-free colony, provided the previous occupants have been separated from such combs, etc., for at least 10 days or a fortnight. This is because the mites cannot live for more than a few days away from the host bee.

The disease is spread by drifting bees ; occasionally by robbing, if the robbed bees, having acarine, join the robbers ; transfer of combs of infested bees to other hives ; and by swarms.

The "crawling" symptom should be confirmed by an examination of the tracheae under a low-powered microscope lens, giving about 10-diameter magnification, before a definite conclusion is reached. The trachea is pearly white in a healthy insect, but in one attacked by the mite, a brown incrustation appears, which gradually darkens and becomes black. At least 30 bees should be examined from each suspected colony.

The dissection is quite simple, but description is not. Briefly, the insect is pinned on its back, on a piece of cork. Then, with the thin blade of a small pen-knife or scalpel, remove the head and first pair of legs by inserting the instrument at the appropriate position and pushing in the direction of the head, rather than cutting. Usually the trachea will now be exposed, and can be examined for the tell-tale blotches. In case of doubt a sample of suspected bees should be sent to an expert for diagnosis.

Treatment of Acarine

Any form of treatment must, to be effective, be designed to kill the mite whilst in the spiracles of the bee, or whilst migrating, without at the same time killing the bee itself. The original method is due to R. W. Frow, but a modification is now necessary owing to shortage of one of the ingredients (safrol) of the mixture used.

The original Frow mixture was:

Petrol .	. 2 parts by volume.
Nitro-benzene	. 2 parts by volume.
Safrol oil	. 1 part by volume.

The modified Frow mixture is as follows:

Ligroin .	. 5 parts by volume.
Nitro-benzene	. 6 parts by volume.
Methly salicylate	2 parts by volume.

The mixtures are inflammable.

Rothamsted recommend the following dosage for colonies moderately affected (less than 25%). Pour 30 minims of the mixture over a flannel pad, distributing the liquid all over the pad, drop by drop. Quietly place the pad over the feed-hole in the crown-board or quilt and cover up. Repeat the dose every other day for seven occasions, using the same pad. Thus 210 minims (3½ drachms) will be used in all. Leave the pad in position after the last dose, for three days, and then remove.

Workers at Rothamsted recommend treatment during February and March, as soon as possible *after* the bees have made their first cleansing flight.

If the disease is discovered in autumn, the methyl salicylate treatment should be applied, as follows:

Obtain a glass specimen-tube, about 2 inches long by ¾ inch diameter, fitted with a cork. Cut a groove in the side of the cork to allow the passage of a small wick. The wick should reach the bottom of the tube amply, and about one inch should protrude from the top of the cork. Fill the tube with methyl salicylate, and allow the wick to become well-soaked. Then roll the tube on its side (horizontally) through the entrance of the hive, about the middle, so that it comes to rest somewhere near the middle of the floor, and thus beneath the middle frame of the brood-chamber. The tube should be left in position until the spring examination, when it is then removed. Thus one prepared tube is required per colony to be treated.

Rothamsted recommend that where diagnosis has shown that 50% or more of the bees are infested, such colonies should be destroyed, as they are a serious source of infestation to other colonies.

For colonies with 25% to 50% infestation (i.e. severe cases) the following treatment is recommended:

Eighty-five minims of the modified Frow mixture is distributed over the pad placed over the feed-hole, and covered up. Two days later repeat the dose of 85 minims on the same pad. Leave the pad for 10 days and then quietly remove it, following immediately with the methyl salicylate "tube" treatment.

The following spring apply the modified Frow treatment as advised for moderately-affected stocks, i.e. seven doses of 30 minims each, leaving the methyl salicylate tube in until the end of the treatment. At the spring examination clear away all dead bees and burn them.

At all times during treatment keep entrances contracted to prevent robbing. Where the treatment is correctly applied, and the dosages are accurately measured, there is no danger to the colony.

Research workers at Rothamsted stress that if all colonies, diseased or otherwise, were treated for three years in succession, the disease would be controlled, and the value of the bees as pollinators and honey producers greatly increased.

Nosema Disease

Nosema disease is not common, but it is widely distributed over the country. The cause is a microscopic animal parasite, *Nosema apis*, which affects the lining of the bee's stomach, destroying stomach cells, and seriously interfering with the bee's digestion. The spores are swallowed by the bee, and hatch out in the mid-gut, where they multiply, form more spores which eventually pass through the rectum, and thus to the outside world.

If the contents of the bowel are voided over stagnant drinking water, or over the face of the comb or elsewhere within the hive, then other bees may become infected by drinking the water, etc.

As the queen does not leave the hive to deposit excreta, any treatment must include re-queening with a disease-free queen.

The symptoms are likely to be confused by the amateur with those for acarine, as in both cases there may be "crawlers." Certain diagnosis can only be made by examination of the stomach contents under a high-powered (1/6th inch to 1/12th inch) lens of the microscope. The spores of *Nosema apis* are oval-shaped, and about four times as long and five times as broad as those of American foul brood.

Symptoms vary, but there are frequently a number of dead bees to be found on the ground in front of the hive; others are in process of being thrown out by the bees. Some other bees may be seen crawling up the blades of grass, and making trembling motions with their wings. Others again may be found dead on the alighting board, lying on their backs with their legs in the air. The intestines are usually quite full, and if pinched the contents of the intestines may shoot out to a distance of some inches. The stock dwindles rapidly at a time when it should be building up.

The symptoms are usually most noticeable in May, but can recur later in the season. In mild cases the following treatment may be carried out: the colony must be fairly strong (as it most certainly will not be if the disease has already taken a good hold). It must be re-queened, well provided with good stores, transferred to a sound, dry hive, and placed on a dry site.

In order to singe all parts of the comb, especially the rims of the cells where traces of excreta may easily lodge, the frames should be lightly blow-lamped. An ordinary blow-lamp is not really suitable for this work, and in Switzerland, where this form of treatment was devised, a special spirit blow-lamp with a small flame was produced. This treatment should be repeated every few days for the space of a fortnight. Any dead or dying bees must be collected and burnt. The old site must be dug over and limed.

A careful watch must be kept, and if the disease does not disappear under treatment, the stock is better destroyed and burnt, together with quilts and combs. The honey is safe for use by the bee-keeper's household only ; it must not be fed to other bees.

The disease is spread by drifting and inter-change of combs. No chemical remedies of any description have been found of the slightest use in controlling the disease, whether applied to feeding syrup or drinking water.

Amoeba Disease

This is an uncommon disease in Great Britain, though several cases have occurred recently. The disease is caused by a parasitic *amoeba* in the Malpighian tubules. The symptoms are that there is a sudden dwindling in the number of flying bees in spring, and infected bees are found crawling around the hive entrance in a dying condition. Reliable diagnosis consists in detecting the cysts of the parasite in the Malpighian tubules.

Bee Paralysis or May Pest

The disease enjoys many alternative names, such as " Black Robber Disease," " Hairless Bees," " Spring

European Foul Brood

Note collapsed larvae, and also healthy sealed cells

Photograph reproduced by courtesy of the Bee Research Laboratory, Rothamsted

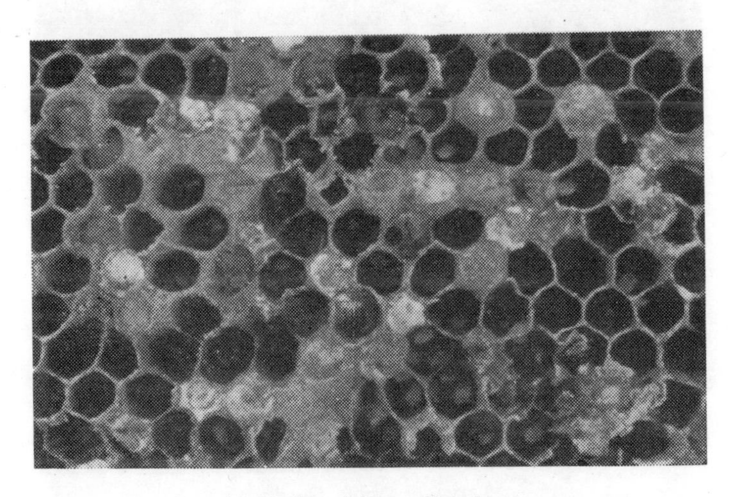

Neglected Drone Brood

Photograph reproduced by courtesy of the Bee Research Laboratory, Rothamsted

Aphids—From the "Shell" film "Protection of Fruit"

Reproduced by courtesy of the "Shell" Film Unit

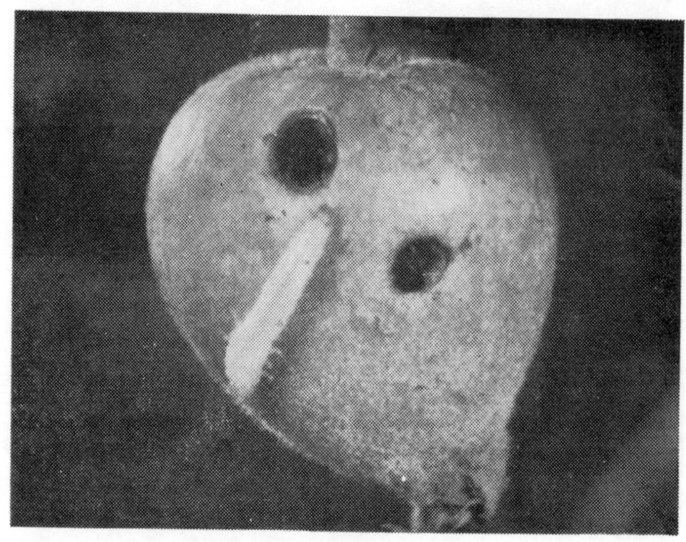

Larva of Apple Sawfly
From the "Shell" film "Protection of Fruit"

Reproduced by courtesy of the "Shell" Film Unit

Dwindling Disease," "Little Blacks," and "May Sickness."

Butler (see *Bee World*, Volume 24, No. 1, January, 1943) has reviewed a number of diseases having similar symptoms (viz., partial or complete paralysis of the affected bee). He has suggested the general term "paralysis" for such cases, and lists nine distinct types, as follows:

1. Infectious
2. Genetical
3. Nitrogen Deficiency
4. Damaged Pollen
5. Poisonous Pollen
6. Poisonous Nectar
7. Poisonous Honeydew
8. Fungal Poisoning
9. Arsenical and other forms of poisoning

From his analysis it appears that many of the types are actually cases of poisoning. For instance, the "damaged pollen paralysis" is probably due to consumption of pollen damaged by frost, and the "poisonous nectar paralysis" may be due to consumption of nectar from certain varieties of cultivated rhododendrons, for example.

In general the symptoms of the infectious, genetical, and nitrogen deficiency types are incidence of black hairless bees; but in the case of the damaged pollen paralysis, the affected bees may not be hairless, but will have dilated abdomens and colons full of ruptured pollen grains.

With the "poisonous pollen" type the abdomens are not swollen, but the bees tremble and cannot fly, affected individuals twirling round on the ground. The symptoms of the "poisonous nectar" variety are body tremblings and a tendency of the affected bees to cluster on herbage near the hive. The bees usually cannot fly.

The "poisonous honeydew" type yields somewhat different symptoms; the affected bees are seldom black or hairless, but cannot fly, and crawl away in all directions from the hive, with their wings sprawled out. Bees affected by the "fungal poisoning" type crawl on the ground and make unsuccessful attempts at flight. Generally their abdomens are distended and colons filled with pollen.

Bees poisoned by arsenical or other substances usually have distended abdomens, are paralysed, and soon die.

Butler states that re-queening a colony suffering from genetical paralysis will effect a cure, but that in the other cases it is only likely to mask the condition. Re-queening, however, can have a beneficial effect even if it does not lead to a direct cure.

The Bee Louse

The bee louse, *Braula coeca*, is a small, brownish-red insect about the size of a pin-head. It attaches itself to the worker and queen bees. Usually only one or two are present on the worker, where the braula exists, but often a queen bee will harbour a score. When present in small numbers it does not appear to be harmful. The lice feed on honey on the tongue of the host. When the hive contains an excessive number of these insects, the cappings of the combs may be damaged by the tunnellings of their larvæ. They may be eliminated from the queen by smoking her gently with tobacco smoke, when the lice will drop off their hosts. Any of the lice present when the Frow treatment is applied are said to be killed by it.

Wax Moth

Two kinds of wax moth are of interest to the bee-keeper, the lesser wax moth, *Achroia grisella*, and the greater, *Galleria cereana*, or, as it is now termed, *Galleria mellonella*. The smaller variety is the more common, and its larvæ do most damage to the combs. This moth is about half-an-inch in length, whereas the greater species is about an inch long.

Achroia grisella, the chief pest, lays its eggs in crevices in the hive, and particularly in the saw-cut made in some types of frame to hold foundation. The larvæ, on hatching from the egg, bore their way through the wax. The use of cloth quilts with this type of frame is very favourable to the moth. The larvæ of the larger variety also consume comb, pollen, and honey.

Strong colonies either eliminate the pest or keep it in check, but a weak stock may have most of its comb ruined. Supers should be treated when stored away for the winter. Naphthalene is of little or no value against wax moth and its grubs. Paradichlorbenzene, better known as P.D.B., is a good fumigant to use.

Place the supers containing the combs in a pile up to a height of about 5 feet, and stick gummed paper round at each junction where the supers meet. Place about quarter of a pound of P.D.B. crystals on a piece of cardboard or paper laid on the top bars of the top-most super. Then put over this a close-fitting roof, making any space at the sides air-tight by stuffing in paper. The crystals slowly volatilise, and the fumes will travel downwards to the floor.

When the crystals have disappeared (and this depends largely on the air temperature) repeat the dose, as any eggs will have survived and hatched out. The stack can be left sealed for three or four weeks, or even the whole winter. *Before use, take down the supers and give them a thorough airing in the sunlight for a few hours to get rid of any fumes, otherwise robbing may be set up in the apiary.*

The work of fumigation is best done in an out-house or bee-shed. Paradichlorbenzene must not, of course, be used directly in a hive containing bees.

VIII—DISEASES OF THE BROOD

Diseases of the Brood

American (or malignant) foul brood; addled brood; European foul brood; chalk brood and sac brood. There are some other troubles, not diseases or pests, which afflict the colony. They are : Dysentery, chilled brood, starvation, dead drone brood, and spray poisoning.

American (Malignant) Foul-Brood

This disease is caused by a spore-forming organism, *Bacillus larvæ*, and both worker and drone brood are attacked, queen larvæ being victims but rarely. Both weak and strong colonies are attacked by the disease, and it is usually the sealed brood which succumbs, normally just after the sealing of the cell. Cases do occur where the pupa form has been reached before death occurs ; and then the pupæ will be found on their backs with tongues outstretched, and likewise in bad cases some dead larvæ may be found unsealed. Careful scrutiny of brood combs should always be made at every examination of a stock.

Symptoms of American foul brood are irregular patches of sealed brood, or even single sealed cells at a time when sealed brood should be absent (as when a stock has been queenless some time, or towards the end of the season when brood-rearing may temporarily cease). The cappings of the cells appear moist and sunken, and some may be perforated due to the bees attempting to remove the infected contents. The larvæ infected pass through well-defined colour changes. When they should be pearly-white they become dull white, then change to a coffee colour, and assume a slimy consistency. Later this dries to a hard brown scale which cannot be removed by the bees.

The " match-stick test " is applied by inserting a match stick into a cell with perforated capping or other suspected cell, and then withdrawing it. An elastic, brown-coloured, " ropey " material is a characteristic of the disease. There may be an unpleasant odour about the whole comb, but sometimes this is not very apparent.

With this disease everything is infectious, brood combs,

honey, brood and super boxes, all hive parts, tools, and the bee-keeper's person if comb or honey has come into contact with him.

The only safe treatment is destruction of the stock, with all combs and quilts. The " shaking " or " saltpetre " methods of treatment, consisting essentially of separating the bees from their comb and brood, are only reliable in the hands of experienced and thoroughly conscientious and reliable bee-men.

European Foul Brood

There may be a number of bacteria concerned in this disease, but one of them, *Bacillus pluton,* is generally accepted to be the causative agent. In this disease the larvæ are normally killed *before* the cell is sealed, when four days old. Some die just after the cell is sealed, but *never spin a cocoon or pupate.* Whereas healthy larvæ are pearly white and plump, diseased larvæ become yellowish and, instead of being in the coiled-up position at the cell base, they make uneasy movements. The colour then changes through light brown to almost black, and the decaying grub has an offensive odour. The " match-stick " test does not yield the long elastic threads characteristic of the American foul brood disease.

There is no effective treatment, and as for American foul brood, bees, brood, combs, etc. must be burnt.

Method of Destruction of Stocks Infected with American or European Foul Brood

As the diseases are spread by robbing, care must be taken to prevent bees from healthy stocks interfering. Contract the entrance to about two inches during the day-time. At nightfall, completely block up the entrance with earth so that no bees can escape, pour in through the feed-hole or quilt about half a pint of petrol, replace the quilt, etc., and close down the hive. Allow about a quarter of an hour for the petrol to kill the bees.

Meanwhile dig a hole at a suitable spot near the hive. This hole should be about 5 feet wide and 2 feet deep. When the bees are dead, remove the combs and stack them in the hole, placing all dead bees, quilts, etc., on top. If the hive is not a sound one, put that on, together with the brood-chamber and excluder in any case. Set fire to the pile of combs, and remain stoking the blaze until everything is completely burnt to ashes. Then at once refill the hole with the soil.

This operation really *must be done when bees are not flying*, as at other times they will surely rob honey from the diseased pile and thus spread the disease.

There is no chemical or drug known, which when fed to the bees in their syrup, or by any other means, can cure either variety of foul brood. Further, it is quite impracticable to sterilise infected combs either by liquids or gases ; such combs *must be burnt*, and no attempt made to save any wax from these stocks.

Sound hives and supers *must* be disinfected before being used again. Unsound equipment should be burnt with the bees, etc. First scrape all wax and propolis from the equipment, burning the scrapings. Then thoroughly flame the equipment with a blow-lamp, until the wood is really scorched and may actually be afire. See that all cracks, corners, and crevices are reached. Then wash all with boiling water to which has been added 1 lb. of washing soda to each gallon. Wash finally with plenty of hot water alone, then air in strong sunlight for a few days. The equipment is then fit for further use. Metal ends should be burnt.

Sources of Infection

There is no completely disease-resistant honey-bee. Safety from the disease lies with knowledge of how it is spread. Scrupulous cleanliness is necessary in all apiary operations. Queen-cells when cut out should not be thrown down on the ground, neither should brace-comb, propolis, etc. Remember honey from infected stocks is a sure means of spreading the disease. It is absolutely safe for consumption within the bee-keeper's household, and it is now illegal to offer it for sale or to remove it from any premises to which the Foul Brood Disease of Bees Order has been applied, solely because, if other bees are allowed to consume it, they will infect their colonies with the disease.

Honey should never be fed to bees unless it is absolutely certain that it came from a healthy stock. Old combs, that is combs without brood or bees, should *never* be purchased or obtained by any means. Bee-men, not absolutely familiar with these diseases and symptoms, should never purchase bees without having a certificate of health, preferably from some independent " expert." Stray swarms of unknown origin should never be obtained. Interchange of combs from colony to colony should not take place unless it is certain such colonies are disease-free. Any second-hand equipment obtained must be disinfected by the process described previously.

The bee-man should be constantly on the watch for disease, and in all cases of doubt, a sample comb should be sent to the staff at Rothamsted, whose services are free to the bee-keeper. And remember, nothing out of a bottle is of any use whatever in these diseases.

Sac Brood

Fortunately this disease is rare in Great Britain. It is caused by a filtrable virus. It is a disease of sealed brood, with symptoms similar to those for American foul brood as far as the appearance of the cappings and age of larvæ attacked are concerned. Diseased combs must be destroyed.

Addled Brood

The cause of this disease is a defective queen. The disease is very common in the British Isles. Both drone and worker brood may be attacked, death normally occurring after the cells have been sealed. The dead pupæ are greyish in colour, and the head and thorax may be apparent but shrivelled. The pupæ shrink to form moist, sticky, brown scales, which, however, do not adhere like scales of American foul brood. The bees attempt to remove the corpses by pulling off the cappings and biting up the remains. The disease is not infectious. The remedy is quite simple and consists in re-queening.

Chalk Brood

The cause of this disease is a mould *Pericystis apis.* The disease is mildly infectious, and is not usually a serious disease. Both worker and drone brood may be attacked. The larvæ die after the cells have been sealed, and form small, fluffy, yellowish-white " mummies." This may be followed by development of spores on the surface of the mummy, in which case the colour changes to greenish-grey or black. The bees frequently remove the cappings and thus expose the " mummies," which then become loose in the cells and rattle when the comb is shaken. The head of the larva can be distincly seen. The " mummies" may be thrown out of the hive by the bees.

Diseased colonies should be re-housed in a dry, sound hive on good combs, and fed. Infected combs should be burnt, and the hive and parts disinfected as for foul brood. Re-queening is also said to be of additional benefit.

Do not confuse mouldy pollen pellets with the "mummies." In case of doubt crush the pellet ; pollen pellets crumble easily.

Other Troubles, Not Diseases

Dysentery

Dysentery is sometimes a sign of other diseases, acarine, etc. The causes of dysentery are many. A damp, cold hive causes the stores to mildew or ferment, and thus leads to consumption of unsuitable food. Fermented honey and honeydew are other causative agents. Feeding with brown sugar or impure sugar leads to dysentery, also feeding syrup to which chemicals have been added. Any disturbance (such as mice) which causes the bees to consume an undue amount of stores during the winter months tends to cause dysentery.

The symptoms are yellow or brown spots on the alighting board and over the hive parts. These spots are due to the discharge of the bowel contents inside and outside the hive. The remedy is to remove the cause of the trouble. A dry, sound hive should be provided, and bees fed in autumn in good time on pure white sugar, cane or beet, to supplement their natural stores. The colonies must not be disturbed during the winter, and entrances must not be so high that mice can enter.

Starvation

The cause of this trouble is lack of stores in the hive. The trouble can occur at any season, even in mid-summer in bad seasons when there is a dearth of nectar.

The symptoms are numbers of feeble crawlers outside the hive, and bees dead in their cells, with their tongues outstretched and adbomens shrunken. The remedy is quite simple ; feed with syrup or honey from a healthy stock.

Chilled Brood

This is not a disease, but usually the result of mis-management by the bee-keeper. The cause is chilling either through loss of bees due to other diseases, or spray poisoning, when there will not be enough bees adequately to cover the brood; or through manipulation and exposure in cold weather. "Spreading the brood," by insertion of empty combs at an unseasonable time, and unsound hives are also contributory causes.

Symptoms are that the pearly-white larvæ change to a glistening black colour, and lie on the bottom of the cells.

Older larvæ assume a grey colour and may later dry up to form a kind of brownish scale. Cappings may appear as in American foul brood, but the "match-stick test" fails to show "ropiness" and of course, *Bacilli larvæ* are absent. Further, all the brood in the affected areas will have died, not here and there as in American foul brood.

The remedy is to manipulate hives at only seasonable times, and to house colonies in sound, damp-proof hives. The bees will themselves clear out the dead larvæ.

Dead Drone Brood

Laying workers and drone-breeding queens produce drones, the larvæ of which sometimes die in the cells and putrefy. The remains become brown and have a peculiar rotten odour. The symptoms are often mistaken for foul brood, but a bacteriological examination will definitely decide. Affected comb should be removed and steps taken to eliminate the laying workers or drone-breeding queen.

Spray Poisoning of the Bee

Considerable confusion exists as to the occurrence of this type of poisoning, and what should be done if and when it has taken place. (See also under Fruit Sprays and Bees). Where arsenic poisoning has occurred, if the scene of spraying was some distance from the apiary, weakening of the colony will be observed, as the foragers die in the fields. Where the apiary is quite close to the orchard, many bees will be found dead and dying in front of the hive.

That brood is found dead in the hive and bees dead outside it, at a time when spraying has taken place, or is taking place, is no proof whatever that the bees or their brood have succumbed to the spray ingredients. Statements to this effect are so often found to be groundless, that genuine cases of arsenate poisoning tend in consequence to be discounted, and so a great deal of harm is done.

After having ascertained for certain that the cause of

death is not some disease, chemical analysis by an analytical specialist should be resorted to. Bee-men may send samples to Rothamsted, where such analysis is done by specialists and at no cost whatever to the bee-keeper. At least 20 of the suspect bees should be sent from each colony concerned, and if brood poisoning is suspected, a sample of brood and, if possible, of freshly-stored pollen taken from the colony concerned. The samples must be accompanied by a letter giving the address of the apiary and date on which samples were taken.

If the bee-man knows definitely that arsenate spraying has taken place, he should mention it, giving if possible the distance of colonies from the orchard in question, the approximate acreage of orchard, and dates of spraying, if known. There is no chemical remedy for the bee against arsenate poisoning. Removal of the apiary to a safe distance until after arsenic spraying has ceased will ensure absolute safety, together with the provision of water within the hive, by means of a frame-feeder.

The question of repellants, etc., is dealt with under "Fruit Sprays and Bees."

IX—PROPOLIS

THE word is derived from the Greek, *pro* meaning "before" and *polis*, "city," and aptly describes its use by the bees. Propolis is a gum obtained from a variety of plants and trees, especially from those whose buds exude a sticky substance. Examples are chestnuts and sycamore.

The colour of propolis varies from yellow to a dark reddish-brown. It possesses an aromatic odour, and although soft at summer temperatures, is brittle when cold. Its melting point is about 150°F. It is soluble in ether and chloroform, partly soluble in alcohol, and very slightly soluble in turpentine. It is insoluble in water, hence one of its uses by the bees to keep rain from entering the hive. The stickiness of propolis varies. The presence of propolis in the modern hive is of little use to the bee-man, as the bees persist in placing it everywhere. One of the chief contaminants of home-rendered wax is propolis.

Many beginners in bee-keeping have received a considerable number of stings, owing to the bees having stuck down the bottom bars of the frames to the floor-board, and on forcibly attempting to remove the frames, the bottom-bar has been left behind and the disturbance angered the bees. With stocks which gather unusual amounts of propolis, it would be found advantageous to smear vaseline over those parts of supers which are in contact.

The mode of loading of propolis is similar to that for pollen. The bee alights near the propolis exuded on the bark of the tree and tears loose a small portion with her mandibles. Drawing this away from the main mass, a thin thread strings out which breaks. With the claws of the mid-legs she removes such threads from her mandibles and deposits them in the pollen-baskets. The mid-legs push the threads into the right position and mould it to the shape of a heap of pollen. This operation is repeated several times until a large drop of propolis adheres to each basket.

The bee takes off for a short flight after tearing loose each piece of propolis, returning after a few seconds to the same place and continuing to load up. The bee returns to the hive when loaded, and several other bees take part in unloading the propolis. The carrier-bee takes a firm foot-hold, and permits the others to extract the propolis from the baskets. Sometimes she is drawn hither and thither in the process. Propolis is often deposited on the entrance boards and left there.

A bee which has returned to the hive under somewhat cold conditions often cannot be freed of her propolis. She spends some time next day on the alighting board sunning herself, until the propolis is ductile enough to be removed.

Bees collect most propolis towards late summer and

autumn. Only when the air is warming up, from about 10 a.m. onwards, does she set out on propolis-hunting expeditions ; a large amount is gathered in the heat of the day, less and less as the temperature falls. Little propolis is gathered during a heavy nectar-flow. Occasionally bees will collect varnish, paint, and even bitumen for use as propolis.

The bees use the propolis in almost every conceivable position in the hive. Sealing down quilts and crown-covers is the main use. Propolis is also used to seal off cracks and crevices, to prevent moisture and draughts entering the hive.

Some races of bees collect more propolis than others, notably the Caucasian bees, which often build a ramp right across the hive just behind the entrance. The propolis they gather is frequently of a slightly different colour and texture from that being collected by other bees at the same time.

The hunting and gathering of propolis is probably hereditary, and the habit is not of much use to the modern bee-keeper. When the bee made its home in the natural state, in any position likely to move or prove draughty, then propolis would considerably help them to provide a sound, dry habitat. If any living thing got in through the entrance, and yet be too large for the bees to remove, such as a mouse or snail, then it would be stung to death and covered with propolis to prevent decomposition odours permeating the hive.

Wax

Although the bee-keeper is mainly interested in wax of insect origin, it is as well to remember that wax can also be obtained from animal, mineral, petroleum, and vegetable sources.

Examples of animal wax are spermaceti, obtained from the skull of a species of whale, and tallow, from the fat of oxen and sheep. Ozokerite is a mineral wax found in the Caucasus, Rumania, and parts of U.S.A. Paraffin wax is an example of the product obtained from petroleum oils. All three waxes find use in commerce and industry.

All vegetables secrete wax more or less upon the seed cases, fruit, or leaves. If one dips a leaf in water and withdraws it, most of the water runs off immediately ; the leaf cannot be " wetted " owing to its waxy nature.

There are many varieties of vegetable wax in commerce. Originally used by the natives as illuminants, they have now found their way into industry. Examples of vegetable waxes are Japanese wax, obtained from the fruits of the *Rhus succedanea*, growing in districts round Nagasaki and Osaka, Japan, and Chinese wax, also obtained from the *Rhus* (but a different species).

Japanese wax has a melting point of about 110°F., and a specific gravity of about 0.975, whilst the Chinese variety has rather a high melting point, 180°F., but a similar specific gravity, 0.970. If Japanese wax is added to bees-wax the resultant product is rendered more brittle and has a lower melting point, hence such addition is worthless.

There is also the palm tree wax from Colombia, which is an exudation from the stems of this palm, the product having a very high melting point, 220°F. From Sumatra comes a wax extracted from the *Ficus*, and having a melting point of 140°F. Growing in Chili and Peru is the Carnauba palm, the leaves of which are dried and the adhering, grey, waxy powder shaken off. It has a melting point of 185°F, is almost as heavy as water (its specific gravity being 0.995), and when added to bees-wax, the product is then harder and of higher melting point.

Bumble bees also make wax, and that of the large red-tailed variety, *Bombus lapidarius*, is a dark-green colour.

There is an insect wax, other than bees-wax, which is of entomological interest. The insect is *Coccus chinensis*, and in spring, scales containing its larvæ are deposited on the twigs and boughs of the Chinese ash tree. These scales are gathered by the Chinese and transported some 200 miles to Chia-tong, the centre of the industry. There they are made up into small packets with leaves and suspended from the ash trees.

The male insect, on emergence, climbs up the leaves and,

reaching the twigs and branches, deposits wax. This deposition extends over about 100 days. When completed the branches are cut down and the wax carefully scraped off. A fresh supply of scales is obtained each year. It is said that 1 lb. of larvæ scales produce 4 lbs. of the insect wax, called Pe La.

Bees-wax is a voluntary secretion of the honey bee, although it cannot be produced at any season. The secretion takes place from the fourth to seventh ventral plates of the abdomen. The wax originates in liquid state in the wax-secreting glands, and is passed into depressed cavities where it is moulded into shape by the segment bearing down on it from above. The liquid solidifies and forms small scales, which the bees withdraw from the wax-pockets.

Only the bees of a certain physiological age can secrete wax. Normally only young bees of between 10 and 17 days of age secrete, but under other conditions older bees can and do produce wax, dependent on the state of gland development.

It is this state of development of the glands that determines whether or not they will function. During the winter months, for example, physiological growth may be considerably retarded so that the glands develop slowly or not at all, consequently the bee during that time does not age, and its powers of secretion are not much impaired.

They must consume a considerably quantity of stores to enable secretion to take place, which occurs after an interval of about 24 hours. The temperature is raised to the neighbourhood of 96° F., partly by consumption of food.

When building or repairing comb, the bees hang vertically in festoons. The scales are scraped off by the hind legs, the spines of the planta (large joint) catching into the scale and moving it up into a position where it can be grasped by the fore-leg. The scale is then manipulated by the mandibles, and a strong salivary juice added rendering the wax more ductile so that it can be placed and moulded as required. Each bee removes its own wax.

Frequently scales may be found scattered on the floor of

the hive, some marked by the spine, evidently dropped in manipulation, and others, being unmarked, have apparently fallen from the bee. Very young bees, and bees over 17 days of age, cannot secrete wax. Secretion only takes place during a heavy honey-flow, or when quantities of food are available.

Various figures have been quoted for the quantity of food consumed to yield one pound of wax, but an average estimate is about 10 lbs. of honey for one pound of wax.

The colour of pure bees-wax is white in comb newly built from syrup, but varies from pale primrose to darker shades, being influenced by the source of food available ; bees working sainfoin, for example, build characteristically yellow comb.

Bees-wax consists of the melissic ester of palmitic acid, together with free cerotic acid. It has a melting point of about 145°F., and a specific gravity of about 0.965. It has the highest melting point for its ductility of any wax known. It is soluble in ether, chloroform, benzene, carbon disulphide, and turpentine, partially soluble in hot alcohol, and insoluble in water and cold alcohol.

Wax, as is well known, is rendered into foundation by milling, the standard process being that of weed. Three-ply foundation consists of a mid-sheet of bees-wax toughened by the addition of a vegetable wax such as carnauba, with an overlay on each side of a sheet of pure bees-wax. To prevent sagging in the hive, and break-down in the machine during extraction, wires are incorporated in the sheets during the process of manufacture.

For those who prefer to wire their own frames—a tedious job—it should be remembered that horizontal wiring is the best method for the amateur, at least three strands for standard and two for shallow frames. The wires must be drawn tight and embedded into the sheets of foundation, preferably by electricity. But ready-wired foundation is best for the busy bee-keeper.

Best combs are obtained by placing the frames of foundation *above* the brood-chamber during a heavy flow, or at a

Winter Spraying—From the "Shell" film "Fruit Spraying"

Reproduced by courtesy of the "Shell" Film Unit

Blossom Time—From the "Shell" film "Protection of Fruit"

Reproduced by courtesy of the "Shell" Film Unit

Pink Bud—From the " Shell " film " Fruit Spraying "

Reproduced by courtesy of the " Shell " Film Unit

Harvest—From the " Shell " film " Production of Fruit "

Reproduced by courtesy of the " Shell" Film Unit

time when syrup can be fed copiously. Under these conditions the combs will be built right down to the bottom bar.

The bee-man should strictly cull poor frames, otherwise there is considerable loss of cell space. Bees will find the wire during a dearth, and in an attempt to remove it, gnaw the foundation away along most of its length. Hence do not leave frames of foundation in hives during unsuitable conditions.

It has been estimated that the cappings from 100 lbs. of extracted honey yield about 1½ lbs. of wax.

Wax Extraction

The solar wax-extractor is a favourite apparatus for rendering comb, but it is really only suitable for dealing with wax from new combs and from cappings. Even then not all the wax is extracted, and steam-extraction should be resorted to. Those which employ steam heating, with pressure, are the most efficient.

The principle is that the wax is contained in a bag, subjected to steam heat, which melts most of the wax. This is drawn off, and then pressure applied to the residue, when more wax is obtained. The pressure is then released, more steam directly applied, and pressure again exerted. This operation is repeated several times, until the maximum amount has been obtained.

The bee-man should be careful not to allow propolis scrapings to get into the wax, as propolis discolours the wax, due to the resinous gums it contains. An average comb is found to contain 96% of wax and 4% of propolis, when carefully scraped and cleaned.

Combs from stocks which have foul brood must *not* be rendered. Such wax *must* be burnt, as there is no process available to the amateur which will sterilise such wax. Burnside has shown that spores heated in wax from foul brood combs for 119 hours at 212°F. still have good growth of *Bacillus larvæ* (the cause of American foul brood) in 60 per cent of the cultures made. In any case, recent legislation has enacted that in cases of foul brood the combs and bees must be destroyed by fire, hence no wax from diseased stocks should find its way into commerce. It is unfortunate that at the time of writing (December, 1943) this order does not apply to Scotland.

Cappings Cleaner

It is necessary that the wax and honey accumulated at extraction time should be dealt with efficiently to prevent robbing. The cappings should be collected and put in a strainer and left all night to enable the honey to drain off. Early next morning the cappings should be given back to the bees to clean up.

A suitable apparatus for this is easily constructed from a super-box. Tack a piece of windolite over the bottom, leaving a space of about 3 inches right across to enable the bees to pass into it. Nail a ramp or weir of wood across the inside of the box in line with the end of the windolite, and about 3 inches high. The cappings may now be scraped into the container so formed, and the box put on the hive.

A crown-board or glass quilt must be placed on top to prevent the bees escaping, or bees entering from outside and robbing. Put on the hive roof and leave for several days, after which it will be found that the bees have removed all the honey and left the cappings dry. Cappings from foul brood stocks must *not* be dealt with in this manner ; they must be *burnt*.

X—PHOTOSYNTHESIS, NECTAR AND HONEY

Nectar

Nectar is the thin, watery sugar solution gathered by the bees from the nectaries of flowers. The nectaries vary in form and position, according to the kind of flower. They are sacs, which become filled with the sugary secretion from special cells, when conditions are favourable. The wall-flower, for instance, has a ring-like nectary at the base of the filament of each short stamen, whilst the buttercup has a nectary at the base of each petal.

To enable life to be maintained and growth and development to proceed, all plants require food. This food they make from the air, moisture, and soil in which they have their roots. A plant growing in sunlight has green leaves, due to the presence of a colouring matter called chlorophyll, which is contained in the cells of the leaves.

If a green plant is put into darkness for several days the leaves turn yellow or even white, owing to the loss of the chlorophyll. Chlorophyll is formed only when oxygen, magnesium, and iron salts are present, and it really consists of chlorophyll A (blue-green), chlorophyll B (green), carotin (orange), and xanthophyll (yellow). A solution of chlorophyll exhibits a condition known as fluorescence; it is green in transmitted light and red in reflected light.

The water necessary to plant life is supplied to the soil by rain, mist, dew, etc. This water dissolves oxygen from the air, and also salts such as nitrates, phosphates, sulphates, and chlorides of sodium, potassium, calcium, magnesium, etc., from the soil. These salts are absorbed by the root-hairs of the plant and are used in making its food.

From carbon dioxide in the air, and water, the plant synthesises (builds up) carbohydrates, a general name given to sugars and starches. Some of the sugar combines with the salts absorbed by the root-hairs to form proteins, etc. The formation of the sugars is of concern to the bee-keeper. The process by which this is done is called photosynthesis, meaning " building up by the aid of light," and sometimes termed " carbon assimilation." The chlorophyll present in the leaf absorbs radiant energy from the rays of the sun, and this energises the carbon dioxide and water to combine, to form sugar and oxygen. The chemical equation is as follows :

$$6\,CO_2 + 6\,H_2O \xrightarrow{\text{Radiant Energy}} C_6H_{12}O_6 + 6\,O_2$$
Carbon Dioxide + Water Sugar + Oxygen

The action very likely takes place in several stages, with the formation of intermediate products, but in broad outline it is as given above. Part of the sugar thus formed is used at once by the plant, for growth, but the remainder is converted by a process of condensation to starch, according to the following chemical reaction :

$$x\,C_6H_{12}O_6 \longrightarrow x\,H_2O + (C_6H_{10}O_5)\,x$$
Sugar Water + Starch

Thus at the close of a sunny day starch can be found in the leaves of the plant. During the hours of darkness this process of photosynthesis ceases, only to re-start when the sun appears again. Thus during dull or cold weather little is produced. During the night the starch is acted on by a ferment called " diastase," present in the leaf cells, and a sugar called " sucrose " is formed, according to the following chemical equation :

$$(C_6H_{10}O_5)\,x + H_2O \longrightarrow x\,C_{12}H_{22}O_{11}$$
Starch + Water Sucrose

Some nectars contain in addition to the sucrose, certain quantities of fructose (lævulose) and glucose.

This sucrose is dissolved in the sap and thus transported to the storage parts of the plant, roots, stems, tubers, etc., and to the shoots and flowers. When the conditions are favourable, the sacs of the nectaries become filled with this sugar solution, which has also absorbed some mineral salts and volatile oils and gums in its passage, together with some of the ferment " diastase," the whole forming the substance called " nectar."

The volume of nectar produced will be governed by a number of factors, of which the weather is one ; and a general review of these has already been given under " The Honey Flow." Some flowers, for instance, the Shirley poppy, do not produce any nectar. It will frequently occur that acres of flowers will be in bloom, but no bees visit them. This is because conditions are such that no nectar has flowed to the nectaries. This is a state of affairs which, in general, is a set-back for flowers as well as bees, since flowers which possess nectaries require the visits of insects for purposes of pollination.

Nature has so placed the nectaries that the insects in their search for nectar come into contact with pollen grains, and as the bees normally visit but one kind of flower on each trip, this pollen is carried to the next blossom of the same variety of plant and thus fertilisation is accomplished.

How Nectar is Carried to the Hive

The bee sucks up the nectar into the honey-sac, the small stomach separated from the larger one by a valve, the "honey-mouth." At the same time as the sac is being filled, the bee adds juices from certain glands. These juices contain digestive agents, including the ferment "invertase." Already the ferment "diastase" is in the nectar, having been derived from the secreting plant. When the sac is fully loaded, the bee returns to the hive and either deposits its load into a cell by applying pressure to the sac, when the nectar is given up again through the mouth, or it gives up its load to another bee, which adds its juices to the liquid as it transfers it to the cell.

Incidentally it can be recorded here that von Frisch has described the honey dance which is performed by a worker who has discovered a new source of nectar. The dance differs from the pollen dance, and von Frisch has named it the "round dance." The bee dances around the comb in various half-circles, first in one direction, and then in another; this causes the watching bees to leave the hive and search for the source of nectar. Françon states that the bees seek out the odour which she gave off with her scent gland, near the source of nectar. The dance is said to last less than a minute, and usually about 25 seconds.

The nectar when collected contains about 80% water and 20% sucrose (identical with household sugar) plus traces of mineral salts, pollen, plant acids, etc. In the cell a fundamental change takes place in the nature and composition of the nectar, brought about by the ferments which the bees have added.

INVERSION

It is stated by some that the excess moisture is removed from the nectar during its change to honey, by an intricate system of bee fanners ; and by others that the product is repeatedly removed by the bees from cell to cell, *via* their honey-sacs. Be that as it may, the water content of sealed honey is on an average about 17%, a considerable reduction.

The change which takes place is the splitting, or " inversion," of the disaccharide " sucrose " to two simple monosaccharides, fructose and glucose, the essential sugars of honey, viz :

$$
\begin{array}{cccccc}
C_{12}H_{22}O_{11} & + & H_2O & = & C_6H_{12}O_6 + C_6H_{12}O_6 \\
\text{Sucrose} & + & \text{Invertase} & = & \text{Fructose} + \text{Glucose} \\
 & & \text{(ferment)} & &
\end{array}
$$

Before a satisfactory explanation of the term " inversion " can be given, it is necessary to describe an instrument which is used in laboratories to evaluate various sugars. This instrument is the polarimeter, and looks like a small telescope mounted horizontally. Instead of the objective and eyepiece of the telescope being made up of a combination of lenses, this instrument has two Nicol's prisms constructed from calcite, and termed the polariser and analyser. The polarising prism is fixed, whilst the analyser is free to rotate.

Now if one looks through the polarimeter from the analyser end, at a source of light placed at the polariser end, when the analyser prism is rotated, it will be found that at one position of rotation, the maximum brightness of light is seen, whilst at another there is total darkness. Intermediate degrees of rotation give all the shades from brightness to total darkness.

When the prism is in the position of total darkness, the Nicol's are said to be " crossed." With the prisms in this " crossed," or dark, position, a standard tube containing a solution of sugar is placed in the polarimeter, in such a position that rays from the source of light, after passing through the polariser, traverse this tube, and then go through the analyser. In general, it will be found that the light appears bright again.

Such substances in solution are said to be optically active. Water for instance, would not affect the light. Sugars and certain organic acids, and many other substances, have this optical power. Having found that the sugar solution is optically active, it will be necessary to rotate the analysing prism, either to the right or left (according to the kind of sugar) to obtain total darkness again.

Using a definite strength of a sugar solution, in tubes of definite length, the rotation necessary is always the same for the same kind of sugar. With certain sugars it is necessary [illegible] the prism to right ; they are said to be " dextro- [illegible] With others it is necessary to turn the prism to the [illegible]se sugars are said to be " lævulo-rotary," different sugars giving different effects.

Certain mixtures, the components of which may contain both dextro-and lævulo-rotary sugars, will cause a rotation either to the right or left, according to which component is the more dextro- or lævulo-rotary. If a solution of sucrose (household sugar, either cane or beet) is placed in the polarimeter, it will be found that it is dextro-rotary, that is, turns light to the right. As the sugar in nectar is sucrose, then it is dextro-rotary. Now as " inversion " takes place when nectar becomes honey, then the rotation will be reversed, or inverted ; that is, honey will turn the light to the left.

Analysis of Honey

An average sample of honey, when analysed, gave the following figures:

Water	17·0%
Lævulose (d-fructose)	39·0%
Dextrose (d-glucose)	34·0%
Sucrose	1·0%
Dextrin	0·5%
Proteins	2·0%
Wax	1·0%
Plant Acids (malic, formic, citric, etc.)	0·5%
Salts (calcium, iron, phosphates, magnesium, iodine)	1·0%
Undetermined Residues (resins, gums, pigments, volatile oils, enzymes, pollen grains)	4·0%
	100·0%

Although lævulose (sometimes known as d-fructose) and dextrose (otherwise d-glucose) have identical chemical formulæ, viz., $C_6H_{12}O_6$, the arrangement of the individual atoms is slightly different in each. It is this slight difference, however, which causes the difference in their optical behaviour.

Dextrose rotates polarised light to the right, as also does the original nectar from which it was derived, but to a different degree. Lævulose, however, rotates light to the left, and this rotation is greater than that to the right; hence honey which contains these two sugars in roughly equal amounts, turns polarised light to the left. Hence the original sugar, sucrose, is said to be "inverted."

It will be seen from the analysis that the ratio of fructose to glucose is approximately 1.1. Any wide variation from this figure would result in honey with different properties and degrees of sweetness, because the two sugars individually process different properties, as shown by the following table:

COMPARATIVE SOLUBILITIES AND SWEETNESS

	Solubility in water at 60°F.	Degrees of Sweetness
Fructose (lævulose) ...	77%	180° (very sweet)
Glucose (dextrose) ...	44%	66° (less sweet)
Sucrose (household sugar)	66%	100° (sweet)

The sweetness was estimated by making up solutions of the sugars to the same concentrations, and then obtaining the opinion of a number of people using a solution of household sugar (sucrose) of equal concentration, as a standard. The results of the sweetness test are interesting, in view of the frequently expressed statement by some people, that they do not like honey because it is so much sweeter than sugar.

Some honeys contain more glucose than the normal, and in view of its much lower solubility, it is to be expected that such honeys would granulate more rapidly. Some glucose may possibly be present, under certain conditions, in nectar when collected by the bees, hence the final product, honey, would contain more glucose than fructose. Honey from some sources in this country may actually granulate in the hive towards the end of July or early August.

THE SUGARS OF HONEY

GLUCOSE ($C_6H_{12}O_6$)

Glucose, dextrose, or grape sugar, as it is sometimes known because of its presence in grapes, occurs together with fructose in most sweet fruits, as well as honey. It is a white, crystalline substance which melts at 187° F.

FRUCTOSE ($C_6H_{12}O_6$)

Fructose, lævulose, or fruit sugar, has the same chemical formula (i.e., the same number of carbon, hydrogen, and oxygen atoms) as glucose, with which it is found in the juices of fruits. It is also present in chicory and the Jerusalem artichoke. Fructose crystallises much less readily than glucose. It is thought that fructose is concerned in the building up of tissue in the body, whilst glucose takes part in the respiratory processes. Glucose is frequently taken by athletes prior to track racing, etc.

Sucrose ($C_{12}H_{22}O_{11}$)

This, as previously stated, is the original sugar of nectar, and this sugar is identical with white, household sugar. The amount found in honey averages up to about 3%. A figure greatly in excess of this amount would probably indicate that feeding had been resorted to when the honey supers were on the hive, or that sugar syrup had been added to the honey. Small quantities of sucrose may always be detected in floral honey, as it seems that the bees do not completely invert all the original sugar.

Sucrose occurs in Nature in the sugar beet and sugar cane, also in the sugar maple and the stems of many plants. It is the most important sugar of commerce.

There are many scores of different sugars ; to name only a few, there is lactose found in milk, raffinose in eucalyptus and cottonseed cake, and galactose, in the form of galactan, in gums and sea-weeds.

Dextrin

This is the intermediate product formed when the insoluble starch is converted by ferments to sucrose (see Photosynthesis). It is a gummy substance (the basis of adhesives) and is found to a very small extent in honey. Honey-dews, however, contain much greater quantities of this substance, a factor which renders honey-dew unsuitable for wintering.

Proteins

Protein materials are built up by the plant from the

sugars formed in photosynthesis and the minerals in the soil which are absorbed by the roots. Proteins are included, with pollen grains and silicates (from the soil) in the colloids of honey. Colloids can be described as particles so tiny that they cannot be removed by the normal process of filtration; hence the cloudy appearance of honey.

This material can be filtered by treatment with special media like bentonite, kieselguhr, or Fuller's earth; but it is possible that the honey loses thereby.

Wax

The wax in honey is accidental, having been derived by the uncapping process. Wax passes through the body without being assimilated.

Plant Acids

These are probably synthesised by the plant, and include malic acid (the acid of apples), citric acids, etc.

Salts

Soils contain many salts, such as compounds of iron, magnesium, silicon, phosphorus, calcium, etc., and these are utilised by the plant in its growth. Hence their presence in the nectar. The varying proportions of these constituents influence the flavour and colour of the final product, honey.

Undetermined Residues

These include gums, volatile oils, and pigments, and are derived from the flower. Pollen grains fall upon the bee and eventually find their way into the stored honey. Incidentally, it is from the analysis of pollen grains (each flower having a well-defined pollen typical of its variety) that we are able to detect the presence of foreign honeys, sometimes used for sophisticating home-produced honey and sold as "English." Should the pollen of a tropical plant be discovered in honey which is stated to be entirely English, then it is reasonable to assume that adulteration has taken place.

The term "undetermined residues" includes many substances about which little is at present known with certainty, such as nitrogenous bodies and vitamins.

Vitamins in Honey

Until quite recently it was not thought that there were any vitamins present in honey, but in 1943, Haydak, of the University of Minnesota, U.S.A., has stated that honey does contain at least traces of six vitamins.

Vitamins are chemical compounds, and some of them are white, crystalline compounds. They are divided into different groups and have well-defined effects on life. The vitamins which have been detected include thiamin (vitamin B 1), ascorbic acid (vitamin C), riboflavin, pantothenic acid, pyridoxine, and niacin. Vitamin B 1 has an influence on starches and sugars consumed in the diet, whilst vitamin C influences the rate of ageing, postponing its onrush, and is effective in reducing the ills caused by the common cold.

The work at Minnesota has established that the filtering process using substances like kieselguhr to clarify honey, removes vitamins at the same time. There is much to be said for leaving natural foods untouched by chemical-physical processes, and the above is a case in point.

Bee-men must be cautious in statements about vitamins in honey. Remembering that the quantity present, if at all, is a fractional amount, they must not make extravagant claims. Honey would still be a most excellent food even if it were proved that no vitamins whatever were present. Water, for instance, is absolutely vital to life. It has no vitamins in it, yet is not eschewed on that account. Much more laboratory work remains to be done, to establish if all or any of those vitamins are present in honey, no matter what its source. At present, the statement concerns honey from various sources in the United States of America.

The Effect of Ultra-violet Light on Honey

Normally, liquids and solids are not luminous. Solids, like iron for instance, radiate light only when heated. If a poker is heated to a high temperature, it exhibits luminosity, becoming red-hot. There are some substances which can be made luminous without any increase in temperature, and the luminosity ceases as soon as the activating agent is removed.

Fluorescein (*Resorcinol-phthalein*) is such a substance when it is dissolved in various liquids, the solutions exhibiting the peculiar effect termed "fluorescence." There are many such substances; for instance, dihydroquinoxalines (organic bodies) possess this property. When rays of light of a certain wave-length meet such liquids, they are absorbed, and immediately re-radiated as light of another kind, or wave-length. The degree of intensity of the flourescence can be increased if the rays of light from an ultra-violet lamp are used instead of sunlight.

Honey when placed under the lamp does not exhibit any particular fluorescence. When, however, a piece of filter paper (non-fluorescent) is dipped vertically in honey, and capillary action draws up some of the liquid, then characteristic zones of fluorescence are exhibited when the rays from the ultra-violet lamp strike the wetted paper. This was first demonstrated by two research workers, Danckwortt and Pfau, who showed that most true (that is floral) honeys exhibited a light-blue fluorescence topped by a white zone, when examined by this method.

Two other workers, Orban and Stitz, carried the method further, and showed that the intensity of the fluorescence depends on the water content of the honey, and hence on its viscosity. They found that the fluorescence was greatest when the honey possessed a low water content and was very viscous. Further, they found that, when the light from the electric spark passing between metallic poles is allowed to pass through a solution of honey, and is then photographed, this light affects the photographic plate in a characteristic manner.

Taken in conjunction with the fluorescent colours obtained, it became possible to determine the approximate origin of a sample of honey examined by these methods. As " artificial honey " is not fluorescent under the conditions of the test, it is therefore obvious that here is another means of detecting serious adulteration of the true floral product.

Viscosity of Honey

Viscosity in honey is its property of flowing slowly or rapidly according to its " body." Bee-keepers confuse density with viscosity, and refer to honey as being " very dense," when what is really meant is that the honey is " very viscous," that is, flows very slowly.

Laboratories have accurate instruments for determining the viscosities of all kinds of fluids. The viscosity of a liquid increases as its temperature falls. A warm honey flows easily ; the same honey when cold would be very slow moving. The principle of the instruments used for this work is the measurement of the time taken for a certain volume of the liquid to flow through a standard orifice. Such instruments are expensive and demand high skill in their use.

Thixotropy

Some liquids, on agitation, become more fluid. Such a property is called thixotropy. Certain heather honeys possess this effect and show a lower viscosity, that is, are more fluid, after agitation, at the same temperature. The fluidity returns to normal after a period of time.

Viscous Honey and Supersonic Waves

As is well known, viscous and thixotropic honeys are difficult to deal with in bulk, particularly when it is desired to transfer large volumes from one storage vessel to another, either by gravitation or by pumping. An attempt has been made to overcome the difficulty by the application of supersonic waves. These waves are elastic vibrations which have a frequency higher than the limit of audibility.

D. W. Gillings, Ph.D., A.Inst.P., in *Chemical Products*, Vol. 7, No. 11–12, Sept.–Oct., 1944, gives an interesting account of these high-frequency waves. He states that, during the study of the physics of submarine signalling, bubbles of gas were liberated from the solution along the path which the supersonic beam of high intensity had travelled. Thus, physical and chemical changes can be brought about by the use of these waves. Small animals can be injured or killed by intense supersonics. Changes can be brought about in certain metal-water and oil-water systems provided that the frequency and intensity are sufficiently high, and solids can be dispersed.

The application of this dispersing action to viscous and thixotropic honeys has been attempted with the object of making their handling easier. Unfortunately, the attempt did not succeed, the transmission of the oscillations apparently being damped by the viscous substance.

As previously stated, density is frequently confused with viscosity. Correctly speaking, density is the mass per unit volume of the substance, and for water this is 1,000 ounces per cubic foot.

It is more usual to refer to the specific gravity of a substance, and this is defined as the ratio of the weight of any volume of that substance to the weight of an equal volume of the standard substance. The accepted standard is water, whose specific gravity is " one." A gallon of water at normal temperature thus weighs 10 pounds, and as the specific gravity of honey is about 1.450, it follows that the weight of a gallon of such honey is about 14½ pounds.

In the units employed by all scientific workers—the centimetre-gramme-second system—density and specific gravity are the same. But there is no connection between viscosity and gravity or density; the former refers to fluidity, whereas gravity or density refers to weight.

Water in Honey

Analysis of many honey samples seems to establish that the water content is normally less than 20%, and usually about 17%. The water content can be determined by the use of a refractometer, an instrument of great accuracy which in effect measures the angle through which light is refracted, or bent, on traversing the sample.

Generally, honey will tend to granulate more rapidly when the water content is lower. Hence a honey with a high water content tends to remain fluid. It is also more susceptible to fermentation.

Granulation of Honey

Granulation is the formation of crystals of the sugar dextrose in the honey. Some honeys form fine granulation, whilst others yield a product with very coarse crystals.

Granulation is a natural event for most honey (except honey from ling) and is, of course, no criterion of purity or adulteration. The dextrose separates in crystal form, rather than the lævulose, simply because the former is less soluble, and readily crystallises, whereas lævulose is very soluble and in any case does not possess the property of assuming crystalline shape.

Granulation is hastened by the presence of minute crystals of dextrose, air bubbles, and the colloidal substances in honey. It can also be induced, at a rapid rate, by agitation. It is a well-known physical experiment carefully to cool water down below its freezing point, when, if all conditions had been favourable, it will remain liquid. But should a shock be transmitted to the vessel containing it, or even coarse-grained dust alight on the surface, crystallisation, that is "freezing," is instantaneous. The study of crystal formation is a science, and there is a lot yet to learn about the granulation of honey.

Honey which granulates is, under certain conditions, liable to attack from ferments. This is because the separation of the dextrose portion as crystals increases the amount of water in the liquid portion remaining. If the water content was already fairly high, about 20%, then the content of water in the residual liquid will be higher and certainly conducive to action by ferments. If, however, the honey had been extracted from sealed combs, this state of affairs will hardly be likely to obtain, on the average.

Granulation, as stated before, is started by the presence of crystals of dextrose. These crystals are in some cases so small as to be undetected by the microscope, but they have the power of inducing crystals to grow.

Crystallisation in other liquids can be induced by seeding them with fine crystals of the substance in solution. It has also been learnt that such crystallisation can be made to take place by seeding crystals, not of the substance in solution, but crystals of another substance, provided that these crystals have the same form as those of the substance in solution. It has been said that the phenomenon applies also to honey, which, it is stated, can be caused to granulate, by seeding with fine crystals of a substance having the same crystalline form as dextrose.

The speed of granulation depends on the quantity of dextrose already in solution, the proportion of lævulose present, and the water content. In general, the greater the amount of dextrose there is, and the less the quantity of lævulose, together with a lower water content, the sooner will granulation commence. And in the above circumstances it is to be expected that granulation would be completed very rapidly.

The proportion of dextrose to lævulose varies with the source of the nectar, and the amount of water normally depends on the climatic conditions prevailing during the season. Hence variations of these three factors within themselves can and do provide various types of honey with differing properties, especially with reference to the granulation process.

There is great diversity of opinion about "clear" and "granulated" honey. Some people prefer one, some the other. The " clear " honey is probably a little more economical in its spreading power, but many will say that the flavour and aroma of granulated honey are superior to that of clear honey from the same source.

Again, a difference in taste exists among devotees of granulated honey. Some prefer a coarsely-granulated product, others honey with a fine grain. Fine grain honey is caused by the presence of a very large number of very small dextrose crystals, when granulation commenced. When there are present only a few dextrose crystals, of a large form, then granulation is coarse, since the dextrose has crystallised in the shape of the large " seeds " which induced the process.

Where an apiary is maintained on soils with a high calcium (iime) content, then charlock and members of the brassica family, if allowed to flower, will yield a coarse-grained honey. There are three methods of dealing with this, should a very " hard " honey be obtained and it is objected to. One is to heat the honey, as honey so treated usually does not granulate again for a few weeks if run into clean, dry, and dustless containers.

Another and better method is to blend the honey with that from another source, a method not always applicable unless the bee-keeper has out-apiaries or can exchange honey with fellow apiarists.

The third method, and one in considerable use in New Zealand and the U.S.A., is to grind the honey in special mills so that fine grains are produced, and the result is a honey with a creamy consistency. The effect can be obtained on small quantities without the aid of a mill, by gently warming the coarse-grained honey and then " whipping " it thoroughly. Adding a small quantity of fine-grained honey from another source will assist the process.

Frosting

This effect is apparent with some honeys which have been bottled immediately from the extractor. Peculiar, white, frothy patches or streaks appear down the inside of the bottle.

Nothing definite is known about the cause, but it is likely that the honey contained a number of air bubbles when run into the bottle, which also may have had imperceptible flecks of dust inside on the glass. These conditions would cause granulation to take place ; the air would be cushioned between the glass and the granules, thus giving rise to the " frosty " effect. Such honey is of course, perfectly good. In fact, it is a sign of its purity, since it has not been " processed " in any way.

Heating and Clarification of Honey

If granulated honey is carefully heated, the crystals will eventually dissolve, and the honey again become liquid. In course of time, however, granulation will again commence.

There is no difference whatever in the food value of liquid and granulated honey, provided neither has been heated. But, if granulated honey, or liquid honey, has been heated, then it must, of necessity, have parted with some of its volatile constituents, and hence there is some alteration in flavour, however subtle.

Further, heating destroys certain other constituents, mostly among the colloidal contents ; and any vitamins if present, would certainly be adversely affected, if not destroyed. If heating is continued beyond 140°F. for any length of time, serious damage is done, the honey being caramelised. Similar words can be written about clarification.

The show " fetish " has produced a type of honey which has been filtered and re-filtered. Some showmen have been known to go so far as to clarify the honey with earths such as kieselguhr and bentonite, which have the property of absorbing colouring matters and other bodies. They also possess the property of removing substances of possible food value, and the Americans have stated that such earths remove any vitamins present. " Super " filtering is neither necessary nor advisable. A filter of cheese-cloth or metal, which will retain the coarse particles of wax, etc., is all that is necessary.

It would be more to the point at honey shows if prizes were awarded to the best-run apiary, and not so much to the best " got-up " sample of honey.

If it should be considered necessary to heat honey, then precautions must be taken to avoid burning, loss of volatile matter, and hence of flavour and aroma. The container should be placed in a vessel of water and must not rest on the bottom of this vessel, otherwise when the latter is heated, local burning of the honey in contact with the bottom of the container will take place, with its certain spoliation. Some small wooden slats should be cut and placed in the pan so that the containers of honey rest on these, thus allowing water to circulate freely beneath the bottom.

The temperature of the honey must not exceed 140°F., and the honey must be continually stirred to enable the melting to take place in the shortest possible time. Keep the container covered between stirs to avoid loss of flavour. As soon as the requisite degree of liquefaction has been obtained, remove the container from the source of heat and seal up. The general rule is, unless it is absolutely necessary to heat honey—don't!

Adulteration of Honey

The blending of foreign honey with, say, English honey cannot be strictly termed adulteration, provided floral honeys alone were employed, and the fact clearly stated. The advantage to be gained by the blender is solely one of price, as pure English honey commands a higher price than foreign or colonial honey, and hence anyone dishonest enough to blend in appreciable quantities of foreign honey stands to gain monetarily ; but the consumer still is eating honey.

Such blending can be detected by an examination of the

pollen grains. All pollens have characteristic sizes and shapes, and research workers have prepared lists of hundreds of pollens. If, then, the pollen of a tropical plant is found in a honey purporting to be of English origin, then blending has taken place.

The addition of syrup and sugars is another matter, as this is sheer adulteration. The biochemist is able, with the aid of his instruments and of certain chemical methods, to detect and accurately state the source and amount of adulterant.

The public should insist that only floral honey, made by the bees from the nectar of flowers, should be classed and sold as honey. Adulteration does go on, and the resultant product is decidedly inferior to floral honey.

Acidity of Honey

Honey is very slightly acidic. Its analysis shows the presence of certain plant acids, such as malic and citric acid. If formic acid is present, it is only there in minute traces, and certainly not as a result of the hoary and ridiculous theory that the bees injected the venom into the honey, for the very simple reason that the bees do no such thing ; and anyway bee venom does not contain formic acid. However, it is important to remember that honey is acidic, and exercise care in the selection of metal honey-containers. Only lacquered tins should be used in which to store honey. Plain tins are slowly attacked by the honey.

The acidity of honey is another pungent reason why all metal vessels which have contained honey should be thoroughly cleaned immediately after use. This particularly refers to extractors, feeders, and storage tanks, which are not lacquered.

Amino acids are also present in honey, due to the breakdown of some of the protein matter by enzymes. These acids are concerned in darkening the honey when it is injudiciously heated.

Poisonous Nectar

It is alleged that certain nectars are either poisonous to the bees or poisonous to man. In the former case, it is hardly likely that man has had an opportunity of tasting the honey produced from such nectar, as the bees themselves would have perished, and it is thought that little or no such nectar would be deposited in the combs. Rhododendrons are thought to be a source of such nectar, and so also are some species of laurel.

Butler (*Bee World*, Vol. 24, No. 1, January, 1943) in listing various types of bee paralysis, cites poisonous nectar as causing a variety of paralysis. He states that the abdomens of poisoned bees are sometimes swollen, the body trembles, and bees tend to cluster together on grass near the hive. The bees are unable to fly, crawl rapidly away from the hive for a short distance, and die.

Poisonous Honey

Rhododendrons have frequently been blamed for poisonous nectar. Xenophon gave an account of the sickness developed during the retreat of the Ten Thousand which occurred B.C.40. F. Kingdom Ward, in his book *Plant Hunter's Paradise*, describes the effects of eating rhododendron honey. He says that the symptoms were similar to acute alcoholic poisoning, and that these passed off in a day or so. The locality was the Tibetan outpost of Tahawndam, and the honey does not appear to affect the natives. In Europe, reports have been received that a few localities in Russia produce such nectar. South Africa, also, has not escaped, poisonous nectar having been found there.

Much work remains to be done to establish the cause of these poisonous nectars ; and it is suggested that attention be given to the mineral content of the soils in which such alleged poisonous plants are growing. It might also be illuminating to examine the plants themselves for glucosides and the presence or otherwise of the enzyme capable of splitting these bodies into glucose and the accompanying organic compound.

It is known that certain nectar-bearing plants, such as lady's slipper (*Lotus corniculatus*) contain a glucoside, whilst botanically identical plants in a neighbouring field are lacking in glucosides.

Influence of Storage on Flavour of Honey

That the flavour of honey improves on storage is well instanced by a letter from Ronald Melville printed in *Nature*, Vol. 154, No. 3916, for November 18, 1944, (*Ailanthus*, source of a peculiar London honey). A sample of honey from a Kensington apiary had a persistent after-taste reminiscent of cats, and this was traced by means of pollen analysis to the nectar from the Tree of Heaven, *Ailanthus altissima*, a tree common in the London streets. Nectar from the sweet chestnut, *Castanca sativa*, also contributed to the after-taste. The flowers of both these trees have an unpleasant odour. Honey from these sources, taken in 1943, was tasted from time to time, and by July, 1944, the unpleasant flavour had disappeared entirely and had been replaced by one of a delicious, rich, muscatel type.

Mr. Melville draws the conclusion that honeys would improve in flavour on keeping, as do those of wines and cheeses. Honeydew is usually blamed for unpleasant flavours in honey, but in this case at least it was not responsible because there were but few mould spores present which grow in the secretion.

XI—FERMENTATION AND ENZYMES

Fermentation of Honey

It is often stated that honey will keep indefinitely. This is only true if " ripe " honey alone is extracted and stored under correct conditions. By " ripe " honey is meant

" sealed " honey, and not the thin, watery, unsealed liquid which has been stored in a tank in the vain endeavour to ripen it.

The fact is that such honey cannot be ripened away from the hive ; and, honey, being hygroscopic, will attract moisture to itself from the atmosphere, and make matters worse. In the sealed and ripe condition, the water content of honey is 17%, and certainly less than 20%. If the water content exceeds this latter figure, then conditions are very favourable to the growth of ferments.

Alcoholic fermentation of honey is the most common. It can occur in both liquid and granulated honey ; in fact, in the latter type it may even be speeded up, owing to the increase in water content of the remaining liquid honey.

Enzymes and Ferments

It was Pasteur, who by his researches on fermentation, showed that micro-organisms were responsible for this phenomenon. Both enzymes and ferments are concerned in the changing of certain substances into others of a totally different kind, for instance, sugar to alcohol, milk sugar to acids (" souring ").

Ferments bring about decomposition in the absence of oxygen and with the evolution of energy, which energy enables the fermenting bacteria to live and increase. Bacteria can be regarded as a low form of plant life and are present in the air. " Alcoholic " fermentation is not produced by such organisms, but by yeast.

An enzyme is a substance produced in small quantities by protoplasm, and has the power of bringing about chemical change in large quantities of certain substances, without itself being affected. Its action is limited to one class of substance ; for instance, the enzyme " lipase " splits fats into glycerine and fatty acids, whilst " diastase " changes starch into sugar. Diastase is produced by the leaf cells of the growing plant, and also by the glands of the worker bee. The sugar (sucrose) of the nectar is broken down or split by the enzyme " invertase," producing the two sugars of honey, fructose and glucose, in approximately equal parts.

Yeast ferment can be destroyed by heat and by powerful antiseptics ; on the other hand, the addition of phosphates to the sugar solution results in fermentation proceeding more rapidly.

The bees need enzymes for the digestion of pollen, their chief source of proteins. After the pollen grain has been broken open by the bee, the contents are digested by the aid of enzymes secreted from the salivary glands. Such enzymes include pepsin and trypsin. These enzymes are vital to life in all its forms. Animals possess them in number, as of course, do humans. For instance, the human stomach possesses a number for aiding digestion ; there are others in the liver and kidneys. Each has its own special work to carry out, and is only found, in general, where that work is to be done. They are generated *in situ* as it were. There are also present in living tissues, complex substances called anti-enzymes, which can upset the action of enzymes.

Enzymes are destroyed by heat, but, strangely enough, resist the action of certain antiseptics which kill ferments, and are adversely affected by very strong substances such as formaldehyde. These antiseptics are of no value in bee-keeping, as damage is done to the bee by their use.

Fermented Honey

The essential features of alcoholic fermentation are the occurrence of numerous bubbles throughout the honey, the presence of froth on the surface, and a characteristic beer-like odour and taste. The bubbles and froth are caused by the evolution of carbon dioxide.

Viscous fermentation can also occur, although it is less frequent and is marked by the formation of dextran, a gummy substance. Viscous fermentation is caused by the presence of certain bacteria, in the absence of air, at relatively high storage temperatures only, 70° to 90°F. Fortunately, it is not very common.

Cause of Fermentation

The yeast content, the water content of the honey, and the storage temperature are three very important factors involved in the fermentation process.

Over the yeast content the bee-keeper has not much control, beyond seeing that his extracting and storing equipment is clean and dry. The amount of water in the honey is under the control of the bees to some extent, and approximates from 15% to about 20% in properly-ripened, sealed honey. Unsealed honey contains water in excess of 20%, and is a potent cause of fermentation.

The storage temperature is most important. The yeasts causing fermentation develop and work at temperatures between 50°F. and 90°F, the most effective temperature being 60°F. Honey stored at low temperatures should not ferment. Granulation may also be delayed under circumstances of *very* low temperatures.

How To Avoid Fermentation

As yeasts are present in the air, in the soil, and in the stems and nectar of the plant, the bee-keeper is powerless to eliminate them. He can only see that he does nothing to add to his difficulties by making sure that his equipment is absolutely clean and dry.

The question of water content is, in a small way, under his control; it being assumed here and now that only ripened sealed honey will be extracted, as this honey alone is fit for storage for any length of time. (See under " Extracting " for a method of determining the suitability of partially-sealed honey).

Make certain that water is not added by a wet uncapping knife. Suitable knives can be obtained, for use cold. Store the honey only in clean, dry, and air-tight containers, as soon as possible after extracting. Store at temperatures below 50°F if possible. Unfortunately most storage rooms are about 60°F, the favourable temperature for fermentation.

Remember that the storage temperature is most important. A clean *dry* cellar, garage, or any other outside, weather-proof building would be very suitable, provided it is quite free from damp. Commercial honey-producers store it in underground rooms, built under their extracting house.

What to do with Fermented Honey

Fermented honey is, in fact, no longer honey, as it is in process of being converted into alcohol and finally becomes acidic in nature. Formic, acetic, lactic, and succinic acids are formed, together with alcohol and carbon dioxide. Such " honey " is unsaleable and unpalatable, and if fermentation has proceeded some way, the material should be used to make honey vinegar, or else destroyed. Bottles, etc., which have held such honey must be thoroughly cleaned and scalded in very hot water.

If fermentation has only just commenced, scrape off the froth, or liquid, in the case of granulated honey, and use the remainder as soon as possible. The material may also be heated in a container in a pan of water, at a temperature not exceeding 140°F, the scum being constantly removed, and the clear remaining liquid used for cooking purposes. The honey container whilst being heated must be stood on wooden slats in the heating pan, to prevent local over-heating of the honey.

The fermentation of honey *can* be prevented by heating and then storing immediately in air-tight containers, but the process requires constant supervision, and at strictly con-trolled temperatures. It is a method definitely not recom-mended to amateurs. (See also " Heating and Clarification of Honey ").

Notes on Storage of Honey

Bottle or can honey as soon as possible after extraction.

Use only dry, clean containers.

Seal the bottles or containers at once.

The use of paper caps is quite safe, provided they adequately cover the top of the container and are well tied round.

Gummed paper is best, if paper is used, and see that it is not wetted by the honey.

Store in a dry, cool place, and occasionally look over the stored containers to make sure fermentation has not developed.

The frothy scum is a sure sign, but occasionally fermentation has been known to proceed from the bottom of metal containers, leaving the top layer still untouched in a granulated condition. The only sure test in these cases is to insert a steel knitting needle. If resistance is constant, all is well, but if the needle sinks in rapidly, suspect fermentation and investigate further.

Sugar for Bees

Although the best food for bees is their natural stores of honey and pollen, occasion arises when it becomes necessary to feed the bees with sugar syrup. It can be stated most emphatically that there is no detectable difference between pure white sugar obtained from the sugar beet and from the sugar cane. Both plants yield sucrose, and the name cane sugar arose some time ago in the early history of sugars, to distinguish it from the totally different grape sugar, obtained, as its name implies, from the juice of grapes. For the last 25 years at least, beet sugar has been increasingly supplanting cane sugar in this country.

The sugar beet can be grown here and on the continent of Europe, and the resultant sugar put on the market at a price comparable with that of the sugar from the canes grown in the West Indies. It is true that its cultivation is subsidised, but the crop is a ground-cleaning one, and hence of value in that direction. Both cane and beet yield sugar which, when refined, contains 99·95% of pure sucrose.

Emphasis must be laid on the statement that pure *white* sugar only, cane or beet, must be used for feeding bees. If brown sugar, or other similar products, be used for autumn feeding, dysentery is certain to follow. No chemicals whatever should be added to the syrup whenever used, nor is it necessary to boil it.

Unblued Sugar

The term "unblued" sugar is given to household, etc., sugar to which no colouring substance of any kind has been added. The final product obtained after processing the canes or beets, is a white, crystalline substance. Some commercial users were not satisfied with this white colour, and after experiments, it was found that the addition of a dye, namely ultramarine blue, gave a product which possessed an enhanced whiteness. The amount of dye added was only from 0·5 part to 5 parts per million parts of sugar, an infinitesimal quantity which could not possibly affect either bees or humans. Some bee-keepers ask for "unblued" sugar, having been misinformed on the subject, but there is actually no need to discriminate.

Honeydew

Honeydew is a dark-coloured, rank-flavoured substance sometimes collected by bees and stored in the comb with true honey. There are two kinds. One occurs on the leaves of trees like lime, sycamore, beech, and oak, and plants such as vetches and field beans. In hot weather the upper surface of the leaves becomes covered with a deposit. The bees collect this, and its flavour and appearance spoil any honey with which it may be mixed.

Also under similar warm conditions, in dry weather, aphides or plant lice (green flies) collect on the under sides of the leaves and on soft stems, and suck out the sap. Their bodies exude honeydew, and this, in the absence of rain which would dissolve it and wash it away, the bees gather. Drought, then, favours the production of both types of honeydew secretions, whilst rain eliminates it.

Whereas true (floral) honey contains only about 0·5%

of dextrin, "leaf" honey, or honeydew, has a much greater amount, a fact which enables the laboratory to differentiate between the two products, apart from taste, etc. Honeydew is unsuitable for the wintering of bees. The honeydew from certain trees, such as the lime (*Tilia platyphyllos*) may cause a type of bee paralysis, listed by Butler as "Poisonous Honeydew Paralysis" (See *Bee World*, Vol. 24, No. 1, January, 1943).

XII—CHEMICALS AND BEE-KEEPING

FROM time to time various chemicals have been stated to be beneficial in bee-keeping. They range from the addition of B-naphthol to syrup as a cure for foul brood, to thymol to prevent the fermentation of the syrup, and even to arrest re-crystallisation of the sugar from the solution.

Let it be said at once that the addition of any chemicals to syrup is not only unnecessary and can serve no useful purpose, but indeed may actually be harmful. The treatment of acarine disease by the Frow formula (and modifications), and the destruction of wax moth by paradichlorbenzene are exceptions, and in any case do not involve treatment of the syrup. These latter are referred to under the "Diseases and Pests of Bees."

NAPHTHALENE ($C_{10}H_8$)

In the past it has been recommended that moth balls (naphthalene) be used to deal with wax moth and its eggs and larvæ. Experience has shown that it has not the slightest effect, the moth grubs attacking the combs in the presence of naphthalene. The remedy for wax moth is paradichlorbenzene, and the method for its use will be found under "Diseases of Bees."

Some books stated that naphthalene would cure or prevent

foul brood. As the spores of the bacillus causing foul brood have successfully withstood the action of formaldehyde solution, an extremely powerful germicide, it is not surprising that naphthalene, a white, crystalline solid derived from the distillation of coal tar, and which only very slowly volatilises, has no effect whatever.

NAPHTHOL-BETA ($C_{10}H_7OH$)

This substance was also stated to cure foul brood if dissolved in methylated spirit and added to the feeding syrup. Although beta-naphthol is soluble in methylated spirit, it is insoluble in water and syrup, so could not possibly be of any value, and it has been proved useless for the purpose by research workers.

THYMOL ($C_{10}H_{14}O$)

This substance has been variously described as a remedy for *Nosema apis*, a preventative of fermentation of syrup, and a chemical to stop the syrup crystallising in feeders. The use of thymol for these purposes is very definitely to be discouraged. It most certainly has no effect on *Nosema apis*, and cannot prevent sugar re-crystallising from syrup in feeders. If too much sugar has been dissolved at a high temperature, it is bound to recrystallise when the temperature falls to that of the hive.

As for preventing fermentation, it has been shown by research workers, that if thymol is added to syrup in sufficient quantities to prevent ferments developing, then the gut of the bee is seriously damaged. Fermentation in feeders can only be prevented by weighing the correct quantity of sugar into measured volumes of hot water, using absolutely clean feeders, and removing them as soon as emptied, or as soon as it is seen that the bees will not take the syrup down, as sometimes occurs in spring stimulation.

Petrol

As its name implies, this is a derivative from mineral (petroleum) oil. Petrol as used for motor spirit has a boiling range of 30°C. to 200°C. approximately (86°F. to 392°F.). It was formerly used in the Frow mixture, but now ligroin is used instead.

Ligroin

A term generally used for a special boiling point petroleum spirit. It has a distillation range of about 90°C. to 120°C. (194°F. to 248°F.), and is, like petrol, highly inflammable.

Nitrobenzene ($C_6H_5NO_2$)

A yellowish liquid with an intense odour of bitter almonds. It solidifies at temperatures below 5°C.

Safrol Oil

A constituent of oil of sassafra.

Methyl Salicylate

This is synthetic oil of wintergreen (the methyl ester of salicylic acid occurs in natural oil of wintergreen) and is a colourless liquid with a wintergreen odour.

Inversion of Syrup

Occasionally the addition of vinegar to syrup has been stated to induce inversion of the sugars, and thus produce a substance akin to the natural food of bees. Vinegar does not produce any appreciable degree of inversion, and is likely to lead to dysentery. Similarly, other acids are equally useless in the concentrations which could be used without damaging the metal of the feeder, as well as the bees.

Disinfectants

In the past, disinfectants of various brands have been added to syrup in an effort to prevent fermentation. Also, such additions to syrup were alleged to have an effect on various diseases of bees. As with other chemicals used for these purposes, disinfectants are useless.

Disinfectants have a use in the apiary, for cleaning up after disease, and one of the best agents to use is bleaching powder. Some precautions should be taken to ensure the most effective use of this substance. Firstly, it should be mixed (it does not entirely dissolve, being a complex substance containing lime and chlorine) with cold or only barely luke-warm water. If warm or hot water be used, much of the effect will be lost owing to the loss of chlorine. Secondly, the solution should be used at once, and not left standing about in buckets for hours, as it slowly deteriorates. Finally, fresh bleaching powder should be used ; old stock, unless kept sealed in a tin, is liable to lose chlorine, the effective disinfecting agent.

Common Salt and Drinking Water

It has often been observed that bees prefer to take stagnant water from farm-yards and pools, rather than pure tap-water. Rothamsted have tested out a number of solutions, and make the recommendation that the only substance which should be added to water for drinking purposes for the bees, is common salt. They recommend that 1 ounce of salt should be dissolved in 6 gallons of water, and this used to supply the drinking places. Incidentally, salt should not be added to the feeding syrup ; it is of no value there whatever.

Chemicals for Nosema Apis

A large number of substances have been recommended as remedies for Nosema, including common salt, Glauber's salt, colloidal silver preparations, gentian tea, tannin, quinine, and mixtures of various herbs. None of these substances is of any value whatever in dealing with this disease.

Bee-Venom

It can be stated at once that there is no detectable trace of formic acid in bee-venom. Much work has been carried out on the determination of the exact constitution of bee-venom, and much remains obscure. So far, it has been determined that one of the compounds which can be isolated from the poison is protein-free, and that a part of the poison is of a lipoid nature. Flury, the worker who discovered this, also found that besides a nitrogenous compound which can be isolated as tryptophane, there are present, glycerin, cholin, palmitic acid and phosphoric acid, etc. There is also a nitrogen-free portion which is the active agent in causing the pain. This is probably a cyclic acid anhydride similar to cantharidin, and in combination with lecithin, causing the inflammation.

For the average bee-keeper a sting is merely an incident, dealt with by immediately scraping it out by the thumb nail. For those unfortunate enough to develop serious reactions to bee stings, the advice is to consult a doctor who is experienced in these matters. Rubbing the affected part with patent medicines is worse than useless.

Preservation of Hives

The modern single-walled hive (National type) must not be painted with oil paints. When constructed of Western cedar, there is no need to coat it with any kind of preservative, but most other timber will require creosoting. Any of the proprietary creosote preparations, or just creosote alone, is suitable.

Creosote can be applied whilst the bees occupy the hive. There is no need, in fact, it is most undesirable, to creosote the inside parts. No amount of airing will eliminate the last traces of the odour of creosote from inside brood-chambers, etc. The older hive—the double-walled type—might well be creosoted rather than painted. Again, only the outer parts should be treated. If this type of hive is painted, then paint must only be applied to the outside.

The objection to painting the modern type of hive is that it may cause the outside combs to mildew in mild, wet winters. The reason for this lies in the composition of the paint, which consists essentially of boiled linseed oil, turpentine, and a pigmnet such as white lead for white paints, or lead chromate for yellow paints. The pigments are there merely to give a pretty colour ; it is the linseed oil which is the preservative.

What happens when wood is painted, is that the turpentine evaporates and the linseed oil slowly oxidises and forms a protective skin. This skin completely covers the area painted, and is impervious to moisture. Hence no rain can get into a wooden structure so preserved. But, the converse also is true, no moisture can get out either ; with the result that any moisture-laden air is retained on the inner walls, a state of affairs which renders the outside combs damp and leads to mildew.

If however, the wood is creosoted, no protective skin is formed, the creosote merely penetrating the wood to a slight extent. Thus the pores of the wood remain open, and allow moisture-laden air to pass slowly through into the outside air. On the other hand, when it rains, the creosote tends to repel the water ; and after the rain has passed the breezes dry the surface of the wood, and such drying tends to bring any moisture in the wood to the surface, where it evaporates.

It has been observed also that oil-painted, single-walled hives often present a blistered appearance in due course, which effect is probably due to the moisture inside attempting to pass out through the walls, and on meeting with the obstructing skin of dried linseed oil, it has in time detached the latter from the wood and so raised the blister.

Much has been written about the effects of creosote on wood, some even alleging that creosote has damaged wood so treated. This is not true of genuine creosote and its modifications. Suffice to say in this connection that many hundreds of miles of railway-sleepers are treated with creosote, in such manner that the liquid permeates deeply into the wood with excellent preservative effect ; if this were not so, the authorities would have given up the process long ago.

XIII—FRUIT SPRAYS AND BEES

Lead Arsenate

References in *The Bee World*, *Bee Craft*, and *The Fruit Grower* have made it clear that there is some concern over the use of lead arsenate and other insecticides in washes for fruit trees. Winter petroleum, D.N.C. petroleum, and tar-oil washes are only applied to fruit crops during the dormant period, i.e. from January to the end of March, and therefore cannot affect honey bees, since there is very little flight during this period.

After bud burst, lead arsenate is applied and this chemical, as is well known, is poisonous to bees. The lethal dose, according to a report from the Annapolis Valley (Dominion of Canada) on pollination and bee-poisoning after spraying, is the minute quantity of about 0·00005 to 0·00008 milligrams of arsenic per bee. Symptoms of arsenical poisoning are described under " Bee Paralysis " in the chapter on the " Diseases of the Adult bee." (Chapter VII).

Lead arsenate is well known to all fruit-growers and its use is confined to well-defined stages of the development of the fruit buds. Its principal use is for the control of leaf-eating caterpillars, such as the winter and tortrix moths, and the grower carefully avoids, in his own interest, applying the wash during the flowering period. Occasionally, an ill-informed grower may spray the trees during the blossoming period, to his and his neighbour's cost. Every effort is made by horticultural advisors and entomologists to discourage this practice.

The use of dinitro-ortho-cresol petroleum winter washes provides a high control of caterpillar, and there are definite signs that the need for lead arsenate spraying will decrease considerably as increased use is made of these washes.

Codling moth of apples and pears in this country is not a pest of great commercial importance, and although lead arsenate is extensively used in the U.S.A. and other apple-growing countries, it is only occasionally used for the control of this pest in this country. Further, the time of application is late June to early July, which is a period when the bees are not attracted to the crop.

On pears, pear slugworm is sometimes a pest and it is controlled by arsenical or preferably derris washes, but these are applied well after the flowering period.

The application of arsenical dusts to fruit crops is very rarely carried out in this country, and it is not officially recommended.

There is some danger in the pre-blossom application of lead arsenate washes to apples, pears, and plums, as it is well known to bee-men that during April and May considerable quantities of water are required by the bees for brood-rearing. The water is obtained from the bark and foliage of the tree, and nectar from weed plants flowering beneath the tree. The bees inadvertently collect arsenical residues which have been deposited on the trees, or have drifted on to the flowers of weeds.

It is probable that the chief danger lies in the deposit on weed flowers, such as dandelion, which are often present on both cultivated and grass orchards. The removal of wild flowers by cultivation in large orchards is not always practicable. The flowering period of the trees is the most attractive period to the bees, during which washes are not applied. Immediately after 80% petal fall, lime-sulphur and nicotine are commonly applied, and at times lead arsenate may be included in the washes. As the washes are applied after petal fall, the risk of poisoning the bee by lead arsenate is considerably reduced, and further, the practice of adding any lead arsenate at this stage is now considered unnecessary.

At petal fall most of the winter moth larvæ are leaving or have left the trees, therefore the pre-blossom application of lead arsenates provides the best control.

In the West Country caterpillars are sometimes blown on to trees that have been winter washed, and therefore on these trees lead arsenate must be applied pre-petal fall, and the recommended stage is pre-blossom.

Generally speaking, fruit-growers avoid spraying during the blossom period because they fear it may interfere with the setting of the fruitlets.

It is, therefore, important that all those concerned with giving advice to growers should stress the importance of bees as pollinators, and as collectors and manufacturers of valuable food, and hence thought must be given in drawing up a spray programme, to avoid poisoning bees.

The subject of lead arsenate poisoning of bees requires investigation in this country, particularly from washes applied before the flowers are open. Investigation on this point would be welcomed by both bee-keepers and fruit-growers, who have a common interest in the bee.

Sprays Other Than Arsenates

Other substances are also used to combat various pests and diseases, and are applied either as dusts or liquids. Fungicides are mainly applied in the liquid form, at any rate, on a large scale, except in such cases as sulphur and copper dusts, which are applied as dry powders. The sulphur is used, for instance, against hop " mould " and gooseberry mildew, and the copper, in conjunction with lime, against potato blight, and for late application to apples and pears.

Liquid fungicides include finely-divided sulphur suspended in water, lime-sulphur, Bordeaux and Burgundy mixtures, etc. The Bordeaux consists of copper sulphate and calcium oxide, and copper sulphate and soda form the Burgundy mixture. Copper fungicides are mainly used against downy mildew of vine, potato blight, and leaf-drop of blackcurrants.

Insecticides are divided into two groups, stomach and contact insecticides, and may be applied either dry or wet. Dry contact poisons include nicotine and nicotine sulphate, (absorbed upon a " carrier ") and derris. They are applied as powders, but do not appear to be used to any great extent at a time likely to cause poisoning to the honey-bee. These same insecticides are also applied in the liquid form. Lead arsenate has already been discussed as a stomach insecticide. These insecticides cause death to the insect through paralysis of its nervous system. Rotenone, the principal toxic constituent of derris and lonchocarpus roots, acts both as a contact and a stomach poison. In the former case, death is probably due to derangement of the respiratory system.

Derris is best applied as a liquid spray to raspberries and loganberries after blossoming, and when the fruit is developing for the control of the raspberry beetle and at this stage bees show no interest in the canes. Workers at Rothamsted Experimental Station have shown that no case of poisoning with nicotine, nicotine sulphate, lime sulphur, or copper has been obtained, either in the laboratory or in cases which have been investigated in the field in this country. Further, they have stated that certain substances, such as lime-sulphur, act as repellants. They have also shown that arsenates have no more attraction for bees than distilled water. Hence arsenate washes should be used whenever possible combined with lime-sulphur, and if possible their use confined to after petal fall.

Water should also be provided within the hive, preferably by means of a frame-feeder, during the period when spraying with arsenates is in progress. By following these procedures, cases of poisoning of the honey-bee by arsenates should diminish.

D.D.T. (Dichloro-Diphenyl-Trichlorethane)

Recent developments in research on insecticides have established that dichloro-diphenyl-trichlorethane, which is relatively non-poisonous to man, may be of considerable value for the amateur fruit-grower both as a stomach and contact poison against many fruit-tree pests, including the larva of the tortrix and winter moths, and apple blossom weevil. It would appear that, as in the case of arsenical insecticides, open blossoms should not be sprayed, owing to possible effects on the honey-bees.

In the *Journal of Economic Entomology*, Vol. 37, No. 1, February, 1944, is an account of the use of this substance popularly known as D.D.T.; and in particular there is a reference by E. C. Holst to work by R. Wisemann on the reactions of honey-bees to dichloro-diphenyl-trichlorethane. Holst extended Wisemann's work, and using caged bees, with controls, found that D.D.T. definitely is a stomach poison for honey-bees at 0·05% concentration, and at 1% acts as a contact poison. Further work is necessary in the field to establish its toxicity to various classes of insects.

Removal of Hives

Where only one or two hives are maintained in or near an orchard where arsenical spraying is part of the normal wash programme, the apiarist is best advised to remove his hives until mid-July. In fact, in the modern, commercial, well-run orchard, there should be little or no forage for the bees after petal fall, as previously stated (see "Sites"). The use of chemicals in syrup to cure the arsenic poisoning after it has been incurred, appears to the author to be a wrong procedure, and not likely to lead to any beneficial results. Should the bees be suspected of arsenical poisoning, the procedure to be adopted is described under "Spray Poisoning of the Bee" page 58.

Fruit-Tree Spraying and Equipment

Effective spraying must be resorted to in order to keep fruit trees in good condition and free from insect pests and diseases. Spraying is not a clean job, and it is a skilled and trying operation, but certainly well worth while. Good equipment is the first essential. Gardeners have quite a wide choice from the lists of manufacturers who cater especially for them, but care must be used in selecting efficient equipment.

For small gardens there are three main types of spray equipment, as follows: (1) Knapsack, (2) Bucket pump, (3) Combined lance and double-acting pump.

1. Knapsack Sprayer

This is filled with the wash, a pressure generated inside the container by pumping in air, and the equipment then carried on the back of the operator by means of slings. The operator then walks up to his bushes and sprays them. Although a pneumatic knapsack sprayer is efficient, it is very expensive, tiring to work, and is definitely not recommended, as the weight of the equipment plus wash tells in time.

2. Bucket Pump

The second type of garden sprayer is exemplified by the bucket pump. A typical one is the A.R.P. pump. In due course, when there is no need to keep it solely for its war-time purpose, this pump, fitted with a special nozzle, will make an efficient double-acting bucket pump. This type requires two operators, which is perhaps a disadvantage.

Both this, and the third type to be described, require a pail or an empty 5 or 10 gallon oil drum as an accessory. If a drum is used, the top should be cut out, two holes punched through near the top rim, and opposite one another, and a carrier made by inserting a sawn-off broom-handle or by lacing some suitable wire-rope. The tank should be placed at a convenient distance, so as to serve as many bushes as possible, having in mind the length of hose available on the pump. The wash can be made up *in situ*, water and concentrate being carried to the tank.

This is better than making up the wash direct in the tank,

and then carrying it to the field of operations, as a full 5- or 10-gallon tank will weigh about 56 lb. or 110 lb. respectively, and some wash may be lost by splashing over when carrying.

3. Combined Lance and Double-acting Pump

This type is most economical as to labour. It is a double-acting pump to which a lance is attached, and it is operated by one person. The cost is about 30s.

The 5- or 10-gallon tank is filled as before, and the end of the hose put in. The lance is held in the left hand, whilst the pumping part of it is operated by the right hand, carrying out an up-and-down movement. By placing the tank in a suitable position, a number of bushes can be sprayed according to the length of the hose available (and capacity of tank).

Of the two latter types of equipment, that requiring two persons is the easier to operate, but the single-operator type (lance with double-acting pump) is the cheaper.

General Hints

See that the equipment is always maintained in good order and condition. Wash it thoroughly after use with cold water; drain all liquid from the pump, hoses, and tank, and store away in a sheltered place. Rubber hoses should not be put away in a position exposed to sunlight.

Winter spraying must be carried out only on suitable days. The trees must be dry, and one must be reasonably sure that rain will not fall before the insecticide has dried on the trees. Washes must not be applied in frosty weather. If a frost appears likely, cease spraying and wait for more suitable conditions.

Spraying in windy weather is a waste of time and material, as the spray is blown everywhere except on to the tree to be washed, and most likely on to a tree already treated, with consequent overdose of oil, which may cause bud-damage.

Make up sufficient spray for the job in hand, and follow the maker's instructions carefully. If made up too weak, it will not fulfil its purpose and hence is wasted. Conversely, if too strong, the result may be serious injury to the trees, with loss of crop.

Apply ample "cover" to each bush or tree. It is not possible to give exact instructions regarding this without seeing each tree. Remember that each branch must be completely covered, and with summer spraying, both sides of leaves, all buds, and fruitlets.

When spraying, commence at the top, and thus drift tends at least to wet the lower branches. Work round the tree until the commencing place is reached. Be sure the underneaths of the branches are covered, and that their tips are adequately sprayed. Spray the trunk right down to the ground. A little too much wash is better than a little too little.

If greenstuffs, etc., are grown beneath the trees, spread sacking over them before operations commence. Incidentally when spraying trees on walls, it will be necessary to use a right-angle nozzle bend on the lance, in order to reach behind the branches.

Winter washes, more especially tar oils, "burn" any grass upon which they fall. The grass soon recovers, however, and nothing need be done about it. Tar oils are trying to the face and eyes, so do not stand so that drift falls on one when using this, or indeed, any insecticide. D.N.C. stains the skin yellow, but hard rubbing with pumice stone in running warm water will remove most of it.

Wear the oldest clothes on spraying jobs. Do the work thoroughly and conscientiously, and results will repay the time, trouble, and money spent.

Pests Controlled

The modern dinitro-ortho-cresol winter wash (popularly known as D.N.C.), if correctly applied at the right time, kills eggs of the winter moth, aphis, apple sucker, capsid bug, and red spider. It also possesses good tree-cleaning properties, destroying the moss and lichen.

Winter spraying of apple trees can be carried out at any time whilst the buds are dormant, that is from January to March, according to the state of the season.

Plum trees should be sprayed as early as possible, in December or early January, certainly not later than first week in February. Trees should be pruned before applying winter wash, and the prunings burnt.

Subsequent spray programmes for the small apple and pear orchard should include a lime-sulphur wash at the pink bud stage, and a nicotine-lime-sulphur wash at petal fall for the apples. If a severe caterpillar attack has developed, then it may become necessary to use lead arsenate, but only at green cluster stage, *not* whilst the flowers are open ; and a repellant wash such as lime-sulphur should be incorporated in the wash.

Winter washes do not affect bees, since the insects are not actively flying during the winter spraying season. The dates and concentrations recommended by the insecticide manufacturers, for spraying against the various pests and diseases, are based on long and careful research work by entomologists and bio-chemists, and hence should be adhered to.

XIV—THE MIND OF THE BEE

Do bees reason ? Can they hear, do they distinguish colours and scents ? These and other similar questions are constantly under examination, and a considerable amount of information has been obtained, particularly on the colour and taste senses of the honey-bee.

At first it would appear that bees are attracted to flowers by the colour. But is it not possible also that the scent has attracted them, or even a combination of colour with scent ?

This question has been investigated by the use of marked bees. From experiments it has been ascertained that bees can distinguish some colours. They confuse certain colours, for instance red and black. On the other hand, they can detect colours which human beings cannot see, such as ultra-violet. Humans are aware of this light by its action on the photographic plate, for instance.

To investigate the sense of scent of the bee, a number of boxes were set out near an apiary. One of the boxes was coloured, the remainder white. The white boxes were empty, the coloured box contained syrup. Soon the bees found this latter box, and visited it for the sugar. Then this box was taken away, and a white one put in its place. Also, one of these white boxes contained a floral scent and some syrup; and soon the bees visited this box only.

To conclude the experiment, boxes were set out, none of them containing any sugar; but one box was coloured and another was white, but contained a floral scent. This time the bees arriving flew towards the coloured box, but when quite near to it, diverted themselves to the scented box. Such experiments show that bees know flowers by their colours, but when in close proximity they know them by their scent.

Has the bee a sense of hearing? No auditory organ has as yet been discovered in the honey-bee.

Are bees intelligent? One is apt to judge intelligence by the speed with which the subject learns. But the matter is more difficult than that. The learning of the art of walking is one of the simplest kinds. Man, many animals, and birds have to learn to use their limbs. Man learns slowly, birds quickly learn to fly. But insects such as bees and butterflies fly perfectly, immediately. Then does intelligence enter into this, with regard to bees?

Instincts do play a great part in the life of the bee. The bee begins life as an egg, from which in time hatches the larva, which eventually becomes a pupa. In course of more time the perfect insect emerges, and at once commences her duties, if a worker. Her jobs change every few days, progressing from cell cleaning, larva feeding, processing the nectar gathered by other bees, wax producer and so on to nectar gathering. The bee carries out all these occupations without having been taught how to do them. This is instinct, not intelligence.

Bees have been found to be able to estimate time. Not however by changes in the world around them, such as lengthening shadows, but by some change in the bee's body cells.

Bees, it is well known, find their way back to their hive when liberated from a distance. But the bees must first have knowledge of landmarks in the vicinity of the hive, or else they fail to return. For instance, bees collected from inside the hive and known to be so young that they have not yet flown, cannot find their way back.

These investigations can quite easily be carried out by the bee-keeper, and very little apparatus, beyond a few saucers and a wine glass or two, is necessary. Much patience is required, and to avoid drawing wrong conclusions, the work must be carried out on marked bees and repeated several times.

BIBLIOGRAPHY

Periodicals

The Bee World, published by the Apis Club, an international paper of high standing, dealing mainly with research and latest methods.

Bee Craft, official organ of the South-Eastern Federation of Bee-keepers' Associations, and many counties.

Bee Keeping, official organ of the South-Western Bee-keepers' Federation.

The Scottish Bee-Keeper, official organ of the Scottish Bee-Keepers' Association.

Gleanings in Bee Culture ; American Bee Journal, published in U.S.A.

Text Books

A.B.C. and X.Y.Z. of Bee Culture, by A. I. Root, Medina, Ohio, U.S.A.

Honey Production in the British Isles, by R. O. Manley.

Anatomy and Physiology of the Honey-Bee, by R. E. Snodgrass.

The Bee Craftsman, by H. J. Wadey.

The Diseases of Bees, published by the Apis Club.

The Mind of the Bees, by Julien Françon.

A Manual of Bee-Keeping, by E. B. Wedmore, C.B.E.

Bee Farming in Britain, etc., by Herbert Mace.

Historical

Bee-Keeping in Antiquity, by H. Malcolm Fraser, Ph.D.

The Sacred Bee in Folklore and Literature, by H. M. Ransome.

Data

Frame Sizes :—

British Standard Brood Frame	...	14 ins. × 8½ ins.
British Shallow Super Frame	...	14 ins. × 5½ ins.
Langstroth	...	17⅝ ins. × 9⅛ ins.
Modified Dadant	...	17⅝ ins. × 11¼ ins.

Metamorphosis of Bees

	Incubation of egg day	Feeding of Larva day	Cell Sealed day	Cell Evacuated day	Bee Flying day
Worker ...	3rd	6th	9th	22nd	36th
Drone ...	3rd	5th	9th	25th	39th
Queen ...	3rd	5th	9th	16th	21st

Weights and Measures

1 Gallon of water at 60°F. weighs 10 lbs.
1 Gallon of honey weighs about 14½ lbs.
1 inch = 2·54 centimetres.
1 metre = 39·37 inches = 3 ft. 3⅓ inches.
1 pound = 0·454 kilogrammes = 454 grammes.
1 kilogramme = 2·2 pounds = 2 pounds 3 ounces.
1 gallon = 4½ litres.
1 litre = 1¾ pints.
1 gallon (Imperial) = 1·2 U.S.A. gallons.

INDEX